LORD KELVIN

Kelvin

LORD KELVIN

AN ACCOUNT OF HIS SCIENTIFIC
LIFE AND WORK

BY

ANDREW GRAY
LL.D., F.R.S., V.-P.R.S.E.

PROFESSOR OF NATURAL PHILOSOPHY IN THE
UNIVERSITY OF GLASGOW

Shadows we are and
Like shadows depart

CHELSEA PUBLISHING COMPANY
BRONX, NEW YORK

The present book is a reprint of a work published at
London in 1908, in the series English Men of Science
under the editorship of J. Reynolds Green, Sc. D.
It is published at The Bronx, New York in 1973 and
it is printed on special 'long-life' acid-free paper

International Standard Book Number 0-8284-0264-7

Library of Congress Catalog Card Number 73-113129

Dewey Decimal Classification Number 530'.0924 (B)

Library of Congress Classification Number QC 16

Printed in the United States of America

PREFACE

THIS book makes no claim to be a biography of Lord
Kelvin in the usual sense. It is an extension of an
article which appeared in the *Glasgow Herald* for
December 19, 1907, and has been written at the
suggestion of various friends of Lord Kelvin, in the
University of Glasgow and elsewhere, who had read
that article. The aim of the volume is to give an
account of Lord Kelvin's life of scientific activity, and
to explain to the student, and to the general reader
who takes an interest in physical science and its applications, the nature of his discoveries. Only such a
statement of biographical facts as seems in harmony
with this purpose is attempted. But I have ventured,
as an old pupil and assistant of Lord Kelvin, to sketch
here and there the scene in his class-room and laboratory,
and to record some of the incidents of his teaching and
work.

I am under obligations to the proprietors of the
Glasgow Herald for their freely accorded permission to
make use of their article, and to Messrs. Annan, photo-
graphers, Glasgow, and Messrs. James MacLehose &
Sons, Glasgow, for the illustrations which are given,
and which I hope may add to the interest of the book.

A. GRAY.

The University, Glasgow,
    May 20, 1908.

CONTENTS

LORD KELVIN

CHAPTER I

PARENTAGE AND EARLY EDUCATION

LORD KELVIN came of a stock which has helped to give to the north of Ireland its commercial and industrial supremacy over the rest of that distressful country. His ancestors were county Down agriculturists of Scottish extraction. His father was James Thomson, the well-known Glasgow Professor of Mathematics, and author of mathematical text-books which at one time were much valued, and are even now worth consulting. James Thomson was born on November 13, 1786, near Ballynahinch, county Down. Being the son of a small farmer he was probably unable to enter on university studies at the usual age, for he did not matriculate in Scotland until 1810. The class-lists of the time show that he distinguished himself highly in mathematics, natural philosophy, and classics.

An interesting incident of these student days of his father was related by Lord Kelvin in his installation address as Chancellor of the University in 1904, and is noteworthy as indicating how comparatively recent are many of the characteristics of our

I

present-day life and commerce.   James Thomson and some companions, walking from Greenock to Glasgow, on their way to join the college classes at the commencement of the session, " saw a prodigy—a black chimney moving rapidly beyond a field on the left-hand side of their road.   They jumped the fence, ran across the field, and saw, to their astonishment, Henry Bell's ' Comet' (then not a year old) travelling on the Clyde between Glasgow and Greenock." [1]   Sometimes then the passage from Belfast to Greenock took a long time. Once James Thomson, crossing in an old lime-carrying smack, was three or four days on the way, in the course of which the vessel, becalmed, was carried three times by the tide round Ailsa Craig.

Mr. Thomson was elected in 1815 to the Professorship of Mathematics in the Royal Academical Institution of Belfast, and held the post for seventeen years, building up for himself an excellent reputation as a teacher, and as a clear and accurate writer.   Just then analytical methods were beginning to supersede the processes of geometrical demonstration which the form adopted by Newton for the *Principia* had tended to perpetuate in this country.   Laplace was at the height of his fame in France, and was writing the great analytical *Principia*, his *Mécanique Céleste*, applying the whole force of his genius, and all the resources of the differential and integral calculus invented by Newton and improved by the mathematicians of the intervening century, to the elucidation and extension of the " system of the world," which had been so boldly sketched by the founder of modern physical science.

[1] Lord Kelvin's address on his installation as Chancellor of the University of Glasgow, November 29, 1904.

In that period Fourier wrote his memoirs on the conduction of heat, and gave to the world his immortal book to be an inspiration to the physical philosophers of succeeding generations. Legendre had written memoirs which were to lead, in the hands of Jacobi and his successors, to a new province of mathematics, while, in Germany, Gauss had begun his stately march of discovery.

The methods and results of this period of mathematical activity were at first hardly known in this country : the slavish devotion of Cambridge to the geometrical processes and the fluxional notation of Newton, an exclusive partiality which Newton himself would have been the first to condemn, led analytical methods, equally Newtonian, to be stigmatised as innovations, because clothed in the unfamiliar garb of the continental notation. A revolt against this was led by Sir John Herschel, Woodhouse, Peacock, and some others at Cambridge, who wrote books which had a great effect in bringing about a change of methods. Sir John thus described the effect of the new movements :—"Students at our universities, fettered by no prejudices, entangled by no habits, and excited by the ardour and emulation of youth, had heard of the existence of masses of knowledge from which they were debarred by the mere accident of position. They required no more. The prestige which magnifies what is unknown, and the attractions inherent in what is forbidden, coincided in their impulse. The books were procured and read, and produced their natural effects. The brows of many a Cambridge examiner were elevated, half in ire, half in admiration, at the unusual answers which began to appear in examination papers.   Even moderators are not made of impenetrable stuff, though fenced with sevenfold Jacquier, and tough bull-hide of Vince and Wood."

The memoirs and treatises of the continental analysts were eagerly procured and studied by James Thomson, and as he was bound by no examination traditions, he freely adopted their methods, so far as these came within the scope of his teaching, and made them known to the English reading public in his textbooks.   Hence when the chair of Mathematics at Glasgow became vacant in 1832 by the death of Mr. James Millar, Mr. Thomson was at once chosen by the Faculty, which at that time was the electing body.

The Faculty consisted of the Principal and the Professors of Divinity, Church History, Oriental Languages, Natural Philosophy, Moral Philosophy, Mathematics, Logic, Greek, Humanity, Civil Law, Practice of Medicine, Anatomy, and Practical Astronomy.   It administered the whole revenues and property of the College, and possessed the patronage of the above-named chairs with the exception of Church History, Civil Law, Medicine, Anatomy, and Astronomy, so that Mr. Thomson became not only Professor of Mathematics, but also, in virtue of his office, a member of what was really the supreme governing body of the University.   The members of the Faculty, with the exception of the Professor of Astronomy, who resided at the observatory, were provided with official residences in the College.   This arrangement is still adhered to ; though now the government is in the hands of a University Court, with the Senate (which formerly only met to confer degrees or to manage the library and some other matters) to regulate and superintend teaching and discipline.

Professor Thomson was by no means the first or the only professor of the name in the University of Glasgow, as the following passage quoted from a letter of John Nichol, son of Dr. J. P. Nichol, and first Professor of English at Glasgow, amusingly testifies :—

"Niebuhr, after examining a portion of the *Fasti Consulares*, arrived at the conclusion that the *senatus populusque Romanus* had made a compact to elect every year a member of the Fabian house to one of the highest offices of state, so thickly are the records studded with the name of the Fabii. Some future Niebuhr of the New Zealand Macaulay imagines, turning his attention to the annals of Glasgow College, will undoubtedly arrive at the conclusion that the leaders of that illustrious corporation had, during the period of which I am writing, become bound in a similar manner to the name of Thomson. Members of that great *gens* filled one-half of the chairs in the University. I will not venture to say how many I have known. There was Tommy Thomson the chemist; William Thomson of Materia Medica; Allen Thomson of Anatomy, brother of the last; Dr. James Thomson of Mathematics; William, his son, etc., etc. Old Dr. James was one of the best of Irishmen, a good mathematician, an enthusiastic and successful teacher, the author of several valuable school-books, a friend of my father's, and himself the father of a large family, the members of which have been prosperous in the world. They lived near us in the court, and we made a pretty close acquaintanceship with them all."

A former Professor of Natural Philosophy, Dr.

Anderson,[1] who appears to have lived the closing years of his life in almost constant warfare with his colleagues of the Faculty, and who established science classes for workmen in Glasgow, bequeathed a sum of money to set up a college in Glasgow in which such classes might be carried on. The result was the foundation of what used to be called the "Andersonian University" in George Street, the precursor of the magnificent Technical College of the present day. This name, and the large number of Thomsons who had been and were still connected with the University of Glasgow, caused the more ancient institution to be not infrequently referred to as the "Thomsonian University"!

The Thomas Thomson (no relative of the Belfast Thomsons) affectionately, if a little irreverently, mentioned in the above quotation, was then the Professor of Chemistry. He was the first to establish a chemical laboratory for students in this country; indeed, his laboratory preceded that of Liebig at Giessen by some years, and it is probable that as regards experimental chemistry Glasgow was then in advance of the rest of the world. His pupil and life-long admirer was destined to establish the first physical laboratory for such students as were willing to spend some time in the experimental investigation and verification of physical principles, or to help the professor in his researches. The systematic instruction of students in methods of experimenting by practical exercises with apparatus was a much later idea, and this fact must be

[1] Successor of Dr. Dick, the Professor of Natural Philosophy who induced the Faculty to grant a workshop to James Watt when the Corporation of Hammermen prevented him from starting business in Glasgow, and for whom Watt was repairing the Newcomen engine when he invented the separate condenser.

taken account of when the laboratories of the present time are contrasted with the much more meagre provision of those early days. The laboratory is now, as much as the lecture-room, the place where classes are held and instruction given in experimental science to crowds of students, and it is a change for the better.

The arrival of James Thomson and his family at Glasgow College, in 1832, was remarked at the time as an event which brought a large reinforcement to the *gens* already inseparably associated with the place : how great were to be its consequences not merely to the University but to the world at large nobody can then have imagined. His family consisted of four sons and two daughters : his wife, Margaret Gardner, daughter of William Gardner, a merchant in Glasgow, had died shortly before, and the care of the family was undertaken by her sister, Mrs. Gall. The eldest son, James Thomson, long after to be Rankine's successor in the Chair of Engineering, was ten years of age and even then an inveterate inventor ; William, the future Lord Kelvin (born June 26, 1824), was a child of eight. Two younger sons were John (born in 1826)—who achieved distinction in Medicine, became Resident Assistant in the Glasgow Royal Infirmary, and died there of a fever caught in the discharge of his duty— and Robert, who was born in 1829, and died in Australia in 1905. Besides these four sons there were in all three daughters :—Elizabeth, afterwards wife of the Rev. David King, D.D. ; Anna, who was married to Mr. William Bottomley of Belfast (these two were the eldest of the family), and Margaret, the youngest, who died in childhood. Thus began William Thomson's residence in and connection with the University of

Glasgow, a connection only terminated by the funeral ceremony in Westminster Abbey on December 23, 1907.

Professor Thomson himself carefully superintended the education of his sons, which was carried out at home. They were well grounded in the old classical languages, and moreover received sound instruction in what even now are called, but in a somewhat disparaging sense, modern subjects. As John Nichol has said in his letters, "He was a stern disciplinarian, and did not relax his discipline when he applied it to his children, and yet the aim of his life was their advancement."

It would appear from John Nichol's recollections that even in childhood and youth, young James Thomson was an enthusiastic experimentalist and inventor, eager to describe his ideas and show his models to a sympathetic listener.[1] And both then and in later years his charming simplicity, his devouring passion for accuracy of verbal expression in all his scientific writing and teaching, and his unaffected and unconscious genius for the invention of mechanical appliances, all based on true and intuitively perceived physical principles, showed that if he had had the unrelenting power of ignoring accessories and unimportant details which was possessed by his younger brother, he might have accomplished far more than he did, considerable as that was. But William had more rapid decision, and though careful and exact in expressing his meaning,

---

[1] A model steam-engine which he made in his youth was carefully preserved by his brother in the Natural Philosophy Department. It was homely but accurate in construction : the beam was of wood, and the piston was an old thick copper penny !

was less influenced by considerations of the errors that might arise from the various connotations of such scientific terms as are also words in common use ; and he quickly completed work which his brother would have pondered over for a long time, and perhaps never finished.

It is difficult for a stranger to Glasgow, or even for a resident in Glasgow in these days of quick and frequent communication with England, and for that matter with all parts of the world, to form a true idea of life and work at the University of Glasgow seventy years ago. The University had then its home in the old " tounis colledge " in the High Street, where many could have wished it to remain, and, extending its buildings on College Green, retain the old and include the new. Its fine old gateway, and part of one of the courts, were still a quaint adornment of the somewhat squalid street in 1871, after the University had moved to its present situation on the windy top of Gilmorehill. Deserted as it was, its old walls told something of the history of the past, and reminded the passer-by that learning had flourished amid the shops and booths of the townspeople, and that students and professors had there lived and worked within sound of the shuttle and the forge. The old associations of a town or a street or a building, linked as they often are with the history of a nation, are a valuable possession, not always placed in the account when the advantages or disadvantages of proposed changes are discussed ; but a University which for four hundred years has seen the tide of human life flow round it in a great city, is instinct with memories which even the demolition of its walls can only partially destroy. Poets and

statesmen, men of thought and men of action, lords
and commoners, rich men's sons and the children of
farmers, craftsmen and labourers, had mingled in its
classes and sat together on its benches ; and so had
been brought about a community of thought and feeling which the practice of our modern and wealthy
cosmopolites, who affect to despise nationality, certainly does nothing to encourage. In the eighteenth
century the Provosts and the Bailies of the time still
dwelt among men and women in the High Street,
and its continuation the Saltmarket, or not far off
in Virginia Street, the home of the tobacco lords
and the West India merchants. Their homely
hospitality, their cautious and at the same time splendid
generosity, their prudent courage, and their faithful
and candid friendships are depicted in the pages of
Scott ; and though a change in men and manners, not
altogether for the better, has been gradually brought
about by sport and fashion, those peculiarly Scottish
virtues are still to be found in the civic statesmen and
merchant princes of the Glasgow of to-day. Seventy
years ago the great migration of the well-to-do towards
the west had commenced, but it had but little interfered with the life of the High Street or of the College.
Now many old slums besides the Vennel and the
Havannah have disappeared, much to the credit of
the Corporation of Glasgow ; and, alas, so has every
vestige of the Old College, much to the regret of
all who remember its quaint old courts. A railway
company, it is to be supposed, dare not possess an
artistic soul to be saved ; and therefore, perhaps, it
is that it builds huge and ugly caravanserais of
which no one, except perhaps the shareholders, would

keenly regret the disappearance. But both artists and antiquaries would have blessed the directors—and such a blessing would have done them no harm—if they had been ingenious and pious enough to leave some relic of the old buildings as a memorial of the old days and the old life of the High Street.

A picture of the College in the High Street has recently been drawn by one who lived and worked in it, though some thirty years after James Thomson brought his family to live in its courts. Professor G. G. Ramsay has thus portrayed some features of the place, which may interest those who would like to imagine the environment in which Lord Kelvin grew up from childhood, until, a youth of seventeen, he left Glasgow for Cambridge.[1] "There was something in the very disamenities of the old place that created a bond of fellowship among those who lived and worked there, and that makes all old students, to this day, look back to it with a sort of family pride and reverence. The grimy, dingy, low-roofed rooms ; the narrow, picturesque courts, buzzing with student-life ; the dismal, foggy mornings and the perpetual gas ; the sudden passage from the brawling, huckstering High Street into the academic quietude, or the still more academic hubbub, of those quaint cloisters, into which the policeman, so busy outside, was never permitted to penetrate ; the tinkling of the ' angry bell ' that made the students hurry along to the door which was closed the moment that it stopped ; the roar and the flare of the Saturday nights, with the cries

[1] Proceedings on the occasion of the Presentation to the University of Glasgow of the Portrait of Emeritus Professor G. G. Ramsay. November 6, 1907.

of carouse or incipient murder which would rise into our quiet rooms from the Vennel or the Havannah ; the exhausted lassitude of Sunday mornings, when poor slipshod creatures might be seen, as soon as the street was clear of churchgoers, sneaking over to the chemist's for a dose of laudanum to ease off the debauch of yesterday ; the conversations one would have after breakfast with the old ladies on the other side of the Vennel, not twenty feet from one's breakfast-table, who divided the day between smoking short cutty pipes and drinking poisonous black tea—these sharp contrasts bound together the College folk and the College students, making them feel at once part of the veritable populace of the city, and also hedged off from it by separate pursuits and interests."

The university removed in 1871 to larger and more airily situated buildings in the western part of the city. Round these have grown up, in the intervening thirty-eight years, new buildings for most of the great departments of science, including a separate Institute of Natural Philosophy, which was opened in April 1907, by the Prince and Princess of Wales.

CHAPTER II

In 1834, that is at the age of ten, William Thomson entered the University classes. Though small in stature, and youthful even for a time when mere boys were University students, he soon made himself conspicuous by his readiness in answering questions, and by his general proficiency, especially in mathematical and physical studies. The classes met at that time twice a day—in mathematics once for lecture and once for oral examination and the working of unseen examples by students of the class. It is still matter of tradition how, in his father's class, William was conspicuous for the brilliancy of the work he did in this second hour. His elder brother James and he seem to have gone through their University course together. In 1834–5 they were bracketed third in Latin Prose Composition. In 1835–6 William received a prize for a vacation exercise—a translation of Lucian's *Dialogues of the Gods* "with full parsing of the first three Dialogues." In 1836–7 and 1837–8 the brothers were in the Junior and Senior Mathematical Classes, and in each year the first and the second place in the prize-list fell to William and James respectively. In the second of these years, William appears as second prizeman in the Logic Class, while James was third, and John Caird (afterwards

13

Principal of the University) was fifth. William and James Thomson took the first and second prizes in the Natural Philosophy Class at the close of session 1838–9 ; and in that year William gained the Class Prize in Astronomy, and a University Medal for an Essay on the Figure of the Earth. In 1840–1 he appears once more, this time as fifth prizeman in the Senior Humanity Class.

In his inaugural address as Chancellor of the University, already quoted above, Lord Kelvin refers to his teachers in Glasgow College in the following words :

" To this day I look back to William Ramsay's lectures on Roman Antiquities, and readings of Juvenal and Plautus, as more interesting than many a good stage play that I have seen in the theatre. . . ."

" Greek under Sir Daniel Sandford and Lushington, Logic under Robert Buchanan, Moral Philosophy under William Fleming, Natural Philosophy and Astronomy under John Pringle Nichol, Chemistry under Thomas Thomson, a very advanced teacher and investigator, Natural History under William Cowper, were, as I can testify by my experience, all made interesting and valuable to the students of Glasgow University in the thirties and forties of the nineteenth century. . . .

" My predecessor in the Natural Philosophy chair, Dr. Meikleham, taught his students reverence for the great French mathematicians Legendre, Lagrange, and Laplace. His immediate successor in the teaching of the Natural Philosophy Class,[1] Dr. Nichol, added

[1] Apparently for a short time in 1841, when Dr. Meikleham was laid aside by illness.

Fresnel and Fourier to this list of scientific nobles : and by his own inspiring enthusiasm for the great French school of mathematical physics, continually manifested in his experimental and theoretical teaching of the wave theory of light and of practical astronomy, he largely promoted scientific study and thorough appreciation of science in the University of Glasgow. . . .

" As far back as 1818 to 1830 Thomas Thomson, the first Professor of Chemistry in the University of Glasgow, began the systematic teaching of practical chemistry to students, and, aided by the Faculty of Glasgow College, which gave the site and the money for the building, realised a well-equipped laboratory, which preceded, I believe, by some years Liebig's famous laboratory of Giessen, and was, I believe, the first established of all the laboratories in the world for chemical research and the practical instruction of University students in chemistry. *That* was at a time when an imperfectly informed public used to regard the University of Glasgow as a stagnant survival of mediævalism, and used to call its professors the ' Monks of the Molendinar ' !

" The University of Adam Smith, James Watt, and Thomas Reid was never stagnant. For two centuries and a half it has been very progressive. Nearly two centuries ago it had a laboratory of human anatomy. Seventy-five years ago it had the first chemical students' laboratory. Sixty-five years ago it had the first Professorship of Engineering of the British Empire. Fifty years ago it had the first physical students' laboratory— a deserted wine-cellar of an old professorial house, enlarged a few years later by the annexation of a deserted examination-room. Thirty-four years ago, when it migrated from its four-hundred-years-old site off the High Street of Glasgow to this brighter and airier hill-top, it acquired laboratories of physiology and zoology ; but too small and too meagrely equipped."

In the summer of 1840 Professor James Thomson and his two sons went for a tour in Germany. It was stipulated that German should be the chief, if not the only, subject of study during the holidays. But William had just begun to study Fourier's famous book, *La Théorie Analytique de la Chaleur*, and took it with him. He read that great work, full as it was of new theorems and processes of mathematics, with the greatest delight, and finished it in a fortnight. The result was his first original paper "On Fourier's Expansions of Functions in Trigonometrical Series," which is dated " Frankfort, July 1840, and Glasgow, April 1841," and was published in the *Cambridge Mathematical Journal* (vol. ii, May 1841). The object of the paper is to show in what cases a function $f(x)$, which is to have certain arbitrary values between certain values of x, can be expanded in a series of sines and when in a series of cosines. The conclusion come to is that, for assigned limits of x, between 0 and a, say, and for the assigned values of the function, $f(x)$ can be expressed either as a series of sines or as a series of cosines. If, however, the function is to be calculated for any value of x, which lies outside the limits of that variable between which the values of the function are assigned, the values of $f(x)$ there are to be found from the expansion adopted, by rules which are laid down in the paper.

Fourier used sine-expansions or cosine-expansions as it suited him for the function between the limits, and his results had been pronounced to be "nearly all erroneous." From this charge of error, which was brought by a distinguished and experienced mathematician, the young analyst of sixteen successfully vindicated Fourier's work. Fourier was incontestably right in holding, though he nowhere directly proved, that a function given for any value of x between certain limits, could be expressed either by a sineseries or by a cosine-series. The divergence of the values of the two expressions takes place outside these limits, as has been stated above.

The next paper is of the same final date, but appeared in the *Cambridge Mathematical Journal* of the following November. In his treatment of the problem of the cooling of a sphere, given with an arbitrary initial distribution of temperature symmetrical about the centre, Fourier assumes that the arbitrary function $F(x)$, which expresses the temperature at distance x from the centre, can be expanded in an infinite series of the form

$$a_1 \sin n_1 x + a_2 \sin n_2 x + \dots$$

where $a_1, a_2, \dots$ are multipliers to be determined and $n_1, n_2, \dots$ are the roots, infinite in number, of the transcendental equation $(tan\ nX)\,/\,nX = 1 - hX.$

This equation expresses, according to a particular solution of the differential equation of the flow of heat in the sphere, the condition fulfilled at the surface, that the heat reaching the surface by conduction from the interior in any time is radiated in that time to the surroundings. Thomson dealt in this second paper with the possibility of the expansion. He showed that, inasmuch as the first of the roots of the transcendental

equation lies between 0 and 1/2, the second between
1 and 3/2, the third between 2 and 5/2, and so on,
with very close approach to the upper limit as the
roots become of high order, the series assumed as
possible has between the given limits of x the same
value as the series

$$A_1 \sin \tfrac{1}{2}x + A_2 \sin \tfrac{3}{2}x + \ldots$$

where A_1, A_2, . . . are known in terms of a_1, a_2, . . .
Conversely, any series of this form is capable of being
replaced by a series of the form assumed. Further,
a series of the form just written can be made to
represent any arbitrary system of values between the
given limits, and so the possibility of the expansion is
demonstrated.

The next ten papers, with two exceptions, are all
on the motion of heat, and appeared in the *Cambridge
Mathematical Journal* between 1841 and 1843, and
deal with important topics suggested by Fourier's
treatise. Of the ideas contained in one or two of
them some account will be given presently.

Fourier's book was called by Clerk Maxwell, himself
a man of much spirituality of feeling, and no mean
poet, a great mathematical poem. Thomson often
referred to it in similar terms. The idea of the
mathematician as poet may seem strange to some ;
but the genius of the greatest mathematicians is akin
to that of the true creative artist, who is veritably
inspired. For such a book was a work of the imagination as well as of the reason. It contained a new
method of analysis applied with sublime success to
the solution of the equations of heat conduction, an
analysis which has since been transferred to other

branches of physical mathematics, and has illuminated them with just those rays which could reveal the texture and structure of the physical phenomena. That method and its applications came from Fourier's mind in full development; he trod unerringly in its use along an almost unknown path, with pitfalls on every side; and he reached results which have since been verified by a criticism searching and keen, and lasting from Fourier's day to ours. The criticism has been minute and logical : it has not, it is needless to say, been poetical.

Two other great works of his father's collection of mathematical books, Laplace's *Mécanique Céleste* and Lagrange's *Mécanique Analytique*, seem also to have been read about this time, and to have made a deep impression on the mind of the youthful philosopher. The effect of these books can be easily traced in Thomson and Tait's *Natural Philosophy*.

The study of Fourier had a profound influence on Thomson's future work, an influence which has extended to his latest writings on the theory of certain kinds of waves. His treatment is founded on a strikingly original use of a peculiar form of solution (given by Fourier) of a certain fundamental differential equation in the theory of the flow of heat. It is probable that William Thomson's earliest predilections as regards study were in the direction of mathematics rather than of physics. But the studies of the young mathematician, for such in a very real and high sense he had become, were widened and deepened by the interest in physical things and their explanation aroused by the lectures of Meikleham, then Professor of Natural Philosophy, and especially (as Lord Kelvin testified

in his inaugural address as Chancellor) by the teaching
of J. P. Nichol, the Professor of Astronomy, a man
of poetical imagination and of great gifts of vivid and
clear exposition.

The *Cyclopædia of Physical Science* which Dr. Nichol
published is little known now; but the first edition,
published in 1857, to which Thomson contributed
several articles, including a sketch of thermodynamics,
contained much that was new and stimulating to the
student of natural philosophy, and some idea of the
accomplishments of its compiler and author can be
gathered from its perusal. De Morgan's *Differential
and Integral Calculus* was a favourite book in Thomson's
student days, and later when he was at Cambridge, and
he delighted to pore over its pages before the fire
when the work of the day was over. Long after,
he paid a grateful tribute to De Morgan and his
great work, in the Presidential Address to the British
Association at its Edinburgh Meeting in 1870.

The next paper which Thomson published, after
the two of which a sketch has been given above, was
entitled "The Uniform Motion of Heat in Homogeneous Solid Bodies, and its Connection with the
Mathematical Theory of Electricity." It is dated
"Lamlash, August 1841," so that it followed the first
two at an interval of only four months. It appeared
in the *Cambridge Mathematical Journal* in February
1842, and is republished in the "Reprint of Papers
on Electrostatics and Magnetism." It will always
be a noteworthy paper in the history of physical
mathematics. For although, for the most part, only
known theorems regarding the conduction of heat
were discussed, an analogy was pointed out between

the distribution of lines of flow and surfaces of equal
temperature in a solid and unequally heated body, with
sources of heat in its interior, and the arrangement of
lines of forces and equipotential surfaces in an insulating medium surrounding electrified bodies, which
correspond to the sources of heat in the thermal
case. The distribution of lines of force in a space
filled with insulating media of different inductive
qualities was shown to be precisely analogous to that
of lines of flow of heat in a corresponding arrangement of media of different heat-conducting powers.
So the whole analysis and system of solutions in the
thermal case could be at once transferred to the electrical one. The idea of the "conduction of lines of
force," as Faraday first and Thomson afterwards called
it, was further developed in subsequent papers, and
threw light on the whole subject of electrostatic force
in the "field" surrounding an electric distribution.
Moreover, it made the subject definite and quantitative,
and not only gave a guide to the interpretation of
unexplained facts, but opened a way to new theorems
and to further investigation.

This paper contains the extremely important theorem
of the equivalence, so far as external field is concerned, of any distribution of electricity and a certain
definite distribution, over any equipotential surface, of
a quantity equal to that contained within the surface.
But this general theorem and others contained in the
paper had been anticipated in Green's "Essay on the
Application of Mathematical Analysis to the Theories
of Electricity and Magnetism," in memoirs by Chasles
in Liouville's *Journal* (vols. iii and v), and in the celebrated memoir by Gauss "On General Theorems

relating to Attractive and Repulsive Forces varying inversely as the Square of the Distance," published in German in Leipzig in 1840, and in English in Taylor's *Scientific Memoirs* in 1842. These anticipations are again referred to below.

CHAPTER III

UNIVERSITY OF CAMBRIDGE. SCIENTIFIC WORK AS
UNDERGRADUATE

THOMSON entered at St. Peter's College, Cambridge,
in October 1841, and began the course of study then
in vogue for mathematical honours. At that time, as
always down almost to the present day, everything
depended on the choice of a private tutor or " coach,"
and the devotion of the pupil to his directions, and
on adherence to the subjects of the programme. His
private tutor was William Hopkins, " best of all private
tutors," one of the most eminent of his pupils called
him, a man of great attainment and of distinction as
an original investigator in a subject which had always
deeply interested Thomson—the internal rigidity of
the earth. But the curriculum for the tripos did not
exhaust Thomson's energy, nor was it possible to keep
him entirely to the groove of mastering and writing
out book-work, and to the solution of problems of the
kind dear to the heart of the mathematical examiner.
He wrote original articles for the *Cambridge Mathematical Journal*, on points in pure and in applied
mathematics, and read mathematical books altogether
outside the scope of the tripos. Nor did he neglect
athletic exercises and amusements ; he won the Col-
quhoun Sculls as an oarsman, and was an active member,
and later, during his residence at Cambridge, president

of the C.U.M.S., the Cambridge University Musical Society.[1] The musical instruments he favoured were the cornet and especially the French horn—he was second horn in the original Peterhouse band—but nothing seems to be on record as to the difficulties or incidents of his practice ! Long afterwards, in a few extremely interesting lectures which he gave annually on sound, he discoursed on the vibrations of columns of air in wind instruments, and sometimes illustrated his remarks by showing how notes were varied in pitch on the old-fashioned French horn, played with the hand in the bell, a performance which always intensely delighted the Natural Philosophy Class.

At the Jubilee commemoration of the society, 1893, Lord Kelvin recalled that Mendelssohn, Weber and Beethoven were the " gods " of the infant association. Those of his pupils who came more intimately in contact with him will remember his keen admiration for these and other great composers, especially Bach, Mozart, and Beethoven, and his delight in hearing their works. The Waldstein sonata was a special favourite. It has been remarked before now, and it seems to be true, that the music of Bach and Beethoven has had special attractions for many great mathematicians.

At Cambridge Thomson made the acquaintance of George Gabriel Stokes, who graduated as Senior

---

[1] The C.U.M.S. began as a Peterhouse society in 1843, and after a first concert, which was followed by a supper, and that by " certain operations on the chapel roof," the Master would only give permission to hold a second concert in the Red Lion at Cambridge, there being no room in College, on condition that the society called itself the University Musical Society. The new society was formed in May 1844 ; the first president was G. E. Smith, of Peterhouse, the second was Blow, also of Peterhouse, a violin player and 'cellist, and the third was Thomson. [See *Cambridge Chronicle*, July 10, 1903, and *The Cambridge Review*, Feb. 20, 1908.]

Wrangler and First Smith's Prizeman in 1841, and eight years later became Lucasian Professor of Mathematics in the University of Cambridge. Their acquaintance soon ripened into a close friendship, which lasted until the death of Stokes in 1903. The Senior Wrangler and the Peterhouse Undergraduate undertook the composition of a series of notes and papers on points in pure and physical mathematics which required clearing up, or putting in a new point of view ; and so began a life-long intercourse and correspondence which was of great value to science.

Thomson's papers of this period are on a considerable variety of subjects, including his favourite subject of the flux of heat. There are sixteen in all that seem to have been written and published during his undergraduate residence at Cambridge. Most of them appeared in the *Cambridge Mathematical Journal* between 1842 and 1845 ; but three appeared in 1845 in Liouville's *Journal de Mathématiques*. Four are on subjects of pure mathematics, such as Dupin's theorem regarding lines of curvature of orthogonally intersecting surfaces, the reduction of the general equation of surfaces of the second order (now called second degree), six are on various subjects of the theory of heat, one is on attractions, five are on electrical theory, and one is on the law of gravity at the surface of a revolving homogeneous fluid. It is impossible to give an account of all these papers here. Some of them are new presentations or new proofs of known theorems, one or two are fresh and clear statements of fundamental principles to be used later as the foundation of more complete statements of mathematical theory ; but all are marked by clearness and vigour of treatment.

Another paper, published in the form of a letter, of date October 8, 1845, to M. Liouville, and published in the *Journal de Mathématiques* in the same year, indicates that either before or shortly after taking his degree, Thomson had invented his celebrated method of " Electric Images " for the solution of problems of electric distribution. Of this method, which is one of the most elegant in the whole range of physical mathematics, and solves at a stroke some problems, otherwise almost intractable, we shall give some account in the following chapter.

This record of work is prodigious for a student reading for the mathematical tripos ; and it is somewhat of an irony of fate that such scientific activity is, on the whole, rather a hindrance than a help in the preparation for that elaborate ordeal of examination. Great expectations had been formed regarding Thomson's performance ; hardly ever before had a candidate appeared who had done so much and so brilliant original work, and there was little doubt that he would be easily first in any contest involving real mathematical power, that is, ability to deal with new problems and to express new relations of facts in mathematical language. But the tripos was not a test of power merely ; it was a test also of acquisition, and, to candidates fairly equal in this respect, also of memory and of quickness of reproduction on paper of acquired knowledge.

The moderators on the occasion were Robert Leslie Ellis and Harvey Goodwin, both distinguished men. Ellis had been Senior Wrangler and first Smith's Prizeman a few years before, and was a mathematician of original power and promise, who had already

written memoirs of great merit. Goodwin had been
Second Wrangler when Ellis was Senior, and became
known to a later generation as Bishop of Carlisle. In
a life of Ellis prefixed to a volume of his collected
papers, Goodwin says :—" It was in this year that
Professor W. Thomson took his degree ; great expectations had been excited concerning him, and I remember
Ellis remarking to me, with a smile, 'You and I are
just about fit to mend his pens.'" Surely never was
higher tribute paid to candidate by examiner !

Another story, which, however, does not seem
capable of such complete authentication, is told of the
same examination, or it may be of the Smith's Prize
Examination which followed. A certain problem was
solved, so it is said, in practically identical terms by
both the First and Second Wranglers. The exam-
iners remarked the coincidence, and were curious as to
its origin. On being asked regarding it, the Senior
Wrangler replied that he had seen the solution he gave
in a paper which had appeared in a recent number of
the *Cambridge Mathematical Journal;* Thomson's answer was that he was the author of the paper in
question ! Thomson was Second Wrangler, and
Parkinson, of St. John's College, afterwards Dr.
Parkinson, tutor of St. John's and author of various
mathematical text-books, was Senior. These positions
were reversed in the examination for Smith's Prizes,
which was very generally regarded as a better test of
original ability than the tripos, so that the temporary
disappointment of Thomson's friends was quickly
forgotten in this higher success.

The Tripos Examination was held in the early part
of January. On the 25th of that month Thomson

met his private tutor Hopkins in the "Senior Wranglers' Walk" at Cambridge, and in the course of conversation referred to his desire to obtain a copy of Green's 'Essay' (supra, p. 21). Hopkins at once took him to the rooms where he had attended almost daily for a considerable time as a pupil, and produced no less than three copies of the Essay, and gave him one of them. A hasty perusal showed Thomson that all the general theorems of attractions contained in his paper "On the Uniform Motion of Heat," etc., as well as those of Gauss and Chasles, had been set forth by Green and were derivable from a general theorem of analysis whereby a certain integral taken throughout a space bounded by surfaces fulfilling a certain condition is expressed as two integrals, one taken throughout the space, the other taken over the bounding surface or surfaces.

It has been stated in the last chapter that Thomson had established, as a deduction from the flow of heat in a uniform solid from sources distributed within it, the remarkable theorem of the replacement, without alteration of the external flow, of these sources by a certain distribution over any surface of uniform temperature, and had pointed out the analogue of this theorem in electricity. This method of proof was perfectly original and had not been anticipated, though the theorem, as has been stated, had already been given by Green and by Gauss. In the paper entitled "Propositions in the Theory of Attraction," published in the *Cambridge Mathematical Journal* in November 1842, Thomson gave an analytical proof of this great theorem, but afterwards found that this had been done almost contemporaneously by Sturm in Liouville's *Journal*.

Soon after the Tripos and Smith's Prize Examinations

were over, Thomson went to London, and visited Faraday in his laboratory in the Royal Institution. Then he went on to Paris with his friend Hugh Blackburn, and spent the summer working in Regnault's famous laboratory, making the acquaintance of Liouville, Sturm, Chasles, and other French mathematicians of the time, and attending meetings of the Académie des Sciences. He made known to the mathematicians of Paris Green's 'Essay,' and the treasures it contained, and frequently told in after years with what astonishment its results were received. He used to relate that one day, while he and Blackburn sat in their rooms, they heard some one come panting up the stair. Sturm burst in upon them in great excitement, and exclaimed, " *Vous avez un Mémoire de Green! M. Liouville me l'a dit.*" He sat down and turned over the pages of the ' Essay,' looking at one result after another, until he came to a complete anticipation of his proof of the replacement theorem. He jumped up, pointed to the page, and cried out, " *Voila mon affaire !* "

To this visit to Paris Thomson often referred in later life with grateful recognition of Regnault's kindness, and admiration of his wonderful experimental skill. The great experimentalist was then engaged in his researches on the thermal constants of bodies, with the elaborate apparatus which he designed for himself, and with which he was supplied by the wise liberality of the French Government. This initiation into laboratory work bore fruit not long after in the establishment of the Glasgow Physical Laboratory, the first physical laboratory for students in this country.

It is a striking testimony to Thomson's genius that,

at the age of only seventeen, he had arrived at such a fundamental and general theorem of attractions, and had pointed out its applications to electrical theory. And it is also very remarkable that the theorem should have been proved within an interval of two or three years by three different authors, two of them— Sturm and Gauss—already famous as mathematicians. Green's treatment of the subject was, however, the most general and far-reaching, for, as has been stated, the theorem of Gauss, Sturm, and Thomson was merely a particular case of a general theorem of analysis contained in Green's 'Essay.' It has been said in jest, but not without truth, that physical mathematics is made up of continued applications of Green's theorem. Of this enormously powerful relation, a more lately discovered result, which is very fundamental in the theory of functions of a complex variable, and which is generally quoted as Riemann's theorem, is only a particular case.

Thomson had the greatest reverence for the genius of Green, and found in his memoirs, and in those of Cauchy on wave propagation, the inspiration for much of his own later work.[1] In 1850 he obtained the

[1] It is rather strange that the ninth edition of the *Encyclopædia Britannica* contains no biography of Green. Born in the year 1793 at Nottingham, the son of a baker, he assisted his father, who latterly acquired a miller's business at the neighbouring village of Sneinton. In 1829 his father died, and he disposed of the business in order that he might have leisure to give to mathematics, in which, though entirely self-taught, he had begun to make original researches. His famous 'Essay' was published by subscription in 1828, and attracted but little attention. In 1833, at forty years of age, Green entered at Gonville and Caius College, and obtained the fourth place in the mathematical tripos of 1837, the year of Griffin, Sylvester, and Gregory. His university career, whatever else it may have done, apparently did not tend to make his earlier work much better known to the general scientific public, and he died in 1841 without the scientific recognition which was his due. That came later when, as stated below, Thomson discovered him to the French mathematicians and republished his 'Essay.'

republication of Green's 'Essay' in Crelle's *Journal;* in later years he frequently expressed regret that it had not been published in England.

In the commencement of 1845 Thomson told Liouville of the method of *Electric Images* which he had discovered for the solution of problems of electric distribution. On October 8, 1845, after his return to Cambridge, he wrote to Liouville a short account of the results of the method in a number of different cases, and in two letters written on June 26 and September 16 of the following year, he stated some further results, including the solution of the problem of the distribution upon a spherical bowl (a segment of a spherical conducting shell made by a plane section) insulated and electrified. This last very remarkable result was given without proof, and remained unproved until Thomson published his demonstration twenty-three years later in the *Philosophical Magazine.*[1] This had been preceded by a series of papers in March, May, and November 1848, November 1849, and February 1850, in the *Cambridge and Dublin Mathematical Journal,* on various parts of the mathematical theory of electricity in equilibrium,[2] in which the theory of images is dealt with. The letters to Liouville promptly appeared in the *Journal,* and the veteran analyst wrote a long Note on their subject, which concludes as follows : "Mon but sera rempli, je le répéte, s'ils [ces développements] peuvent aider à bien faire comprendre la haute importance du travail de ce jeune géomètre, et si M. Thomson lui-même veut bien y voir une preuve nouvelle de l'amitié que je lui porte et de l'estime qui j'ai pour son talent."

[1] January 1869, *Reprint,* etc., Article XV.   [2] *Reprint,* Article V.

The method of images may be regarded as a development in a particular direction of the paper "On the Uniform Motion of Heat" already referred to, and, taken along with this latter paper, forms the most striking indication afforded by the whole range of Thomson's earlier work of the strength and originality of his mathematical genius. Accordingly a chapter is here devoted to a more complete explanation of the first paper and the developments which flowed from it. The general reader may pass over the chapter, and return to it from time to time as he finds opportunity, until it is completely understood.

CHAPTER IV

THE MATHEMATICAL THEORY OF ELECTRICITY IN EQUI-
LIBRIUM. ELECTRIC IMAGES. ELECTRIC INVERSION

In describing Thomson's early electrical researches we
shall not enter into detailed calculations, but merely
explain the methods employed. The meaning of certain
technical terms may be recalled in the first place.

The whole space in which a distribution of electricity produces any action on electrified bodies is called
the *electrical field* of the distribution. The force
exerted on a very small insulated trial conductor, on
which is an electric charge of amount equal to that
taken as the unit quantity of electricity, measures the
field-intensity at any point at which the conductor is
placed. The direction of the field-intensity at the
point is that in which the small conductor is there
urged. If the charge on the small conductor were a
negative unit, instead of a positive, the direction of
the force would be reversed; the magnitude of the
force would remain the same. To make the field-
intensity quite definite, a positive unit is chosen for its
specification. For a charge on the trial-conductor
consisting of any number of units, the force is that
number of times the field-intensity. The field-
intensity is often specified by its components, X, Y, Z
in three chosen directions at right angles to one
another.

Now in all cases in which the action, whether attraction or repulsion, between two unit quantities of matter concentrated at points is inversely as the square of the distance between the charges, the field-intensity, or its components, can be found from a certain function V of the charges forming the acting distribution [which is always capable of being regarded for mathematical purposes as a system of small charges existing at points of space, *point-charges* we shall call them], their positions, and the position of the point at which the field-intensity is to be found. If q_1, q_2, . . . be the point-charges, and be positive when the charges are positive and negative when the charges are negative, and r_1, r_2, . . . be their distances from the point P, V is $q_1/r_1 + q_2/r_2 + \ldots$ The field-intensity is the rate of diminution of the value of V at P, taken along the specified direction. The three gradients parallel to the three chosen coordinate directions are X, Y, Z; but for their calculation it is necessary to insert the values of r_1, r_2, . . . in terms of the coordinates which specify the positions of the point-charges, and the coordinates x, y, z which specify the position of P. Once this is done, X, Y, Z are obtained by a simple systematic process of calculation, namely, differentiation of the function V with respect to x, y, z.

This function V seems to have been first used by Laplace for gravitational matter in the *Mécanique Céleste*; its importance for electricity and magnetism was recognised by Green, who named it the *potential*. It has an important physical signification. It represents the work which would have to be done to bring a unit of positive electricity, against the electrical repulsion of the distribution, up to the point P from a point at an infinite distance from every part of the distribution; or, in other words, what we now call the *potential energy* of a charge q situated at P is qV. The excess of the potential at P, over the potential at any other point Q in the field, is the work which must be spent in carrying a positive unit from Q to P against electrical repulsion. Of course, if the force to be overcome from Q to P is on the whole an attraction, work has not been spent in effecting the transference, but gained by allowing it to take place. The difference of potential is then negative, that is, the potential of Q is higher than that of P.

The difference of potential depends only on the points P and Q, and not at all on the path pursued between them. Thus, if a unit of electricity be carried from P to Q by any path, and back by any other, no work is done on the whole by the agent carrying the unit. This simple fact precludes the possibility of obtaining a so-called perpetual motion (a self-acting machine doing useful work) by means of electrical action. The same thing is true *mutatis mutandis* of gravitational action.

In the thermal analogy explained by Thomson in his first paper, the positive point-charges are point-sources of heat, which is there poured at constant rate into the medium (supposed of uniform quality) to be drawn off in part from the medium at constant rate where there are *sinks* (or negative sources),—the negative point-charges in the electrical case,—while the remainder is conducted away to more and more distant parts of the conducting medium supposed infinitely extended. Whenever a point-source, or a point-sink, exists at a distance from other sources or sinks, the flow in the vicinity is in straight lines from or to the point, and these straight lines would be indefinitely extended if either source or sink existed by itself. As it is, the direction and amount of flow everywhere depends on the flow resulting from the whole arrangement of sources and sinks. Lines can be drawn in the medium which show the direction of the resultant flow from point to point, and these lines of flow can be so spaced as to indicate, by their closeness together or their distance apart, where the rate of flow is greater or smaller ; and such lines start from sources, and either end in sinks or continue their course to infinity. In the electrical case these lines are the analogues of the lines of electric force (or field-intensity) in the insulating medium, which start from positive charges and end in negative, or are prolonged to infinity.

Across such lines of flow can be drawn a family of surfaces, to each of which the lines met by the surface are perpendicular. These surfaces are the equitemperature surfaces, or, as they are usually called, the isothermal surfaces. They can be drawn more closely crowded together, or more widely separated, so as to indicate where the rate of falling off of temperature (the " temperature slope ") is greater or less, just as the contour lines in a map show the slopes on a hill-side.

Instead of the thermal analogy might have been used equally well that of steady flow in an indefinitely extended mass of homogeneous frictionless and incompressible fluid, into which fluid is being poured at a constant rate by sources and withdrawn by sinks. The isothermal surfaces are replaced by surfaces of equal pressure, while lines of flow in one are also lines of flow in the other.

Now let heat be poured into the medium at constant rate by a single point-source P (Fig. 1), and drawn off at a smaller rate by a single point-sink P', while the remainder flows to more and more remote parts of the medium, supposed infinite in extent in every direction. After a sufficient time from the beginning of the flow a definite system of lines of flow and isothermal sur- faces can be traced for this case in the man- ner described above. One of the isothermal

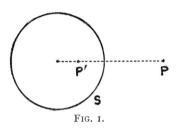

FIG. 1.

surfaces will be a sphere S surrounding the sink, which, however, will not be at the centre of the sphere, but so situated that the source, sink, and centre are in line, and that the radius of the sphere is a mean proportional between the distances of the source and sink from the centre. If a be the radius of the sphere and f the distance of the source from the centre of the sphere, the heat carried off by the sink is the fraction a/f of that given out by the source.

In the electrical analogue, the source and sink are respectively a point-charge and what is called the "electric image" of that charge with respect to the sphere, which is in this case an equipotential surface. And just as the lines of flow of heat meet the spherical isothermal surface at right angles, so the lines of force in the electrical case meet the equipotential surface also at right angles. Now obviously in the thermal case a spherical sink could be arranged coinciding with the spherical surface so as to receive the flow there arriving and carry off the heat from the medium, without in the least disturbing the flow outside the sphere. The whole amount of heat arriving would be the same : the amount received per unit area at any point on the sphere would evidently be proportional to the gradient of temperature there towards the surface. Of course the same thing could be done at any isothermal surface, and the same proportionality would hold in that case.

Similarly the source could be replaced by a surface-distribution of sources over any surrounding isothermal surface ; and the condition to be fulfilled in that case would be that the amount of heat given out per unit area anywhere should be exactly that which flows out along the lines of flow there in the actual case. Outside the surface the field of flow would not be affected by this replacement. It is obvious that in this case the outflow per unit area must be proportional to the temperature slope outward from the surface.

The same statements hold for any complex system of sources and sinks. There must be the same outflow from the isothermal surface or inflow towards it, as there is in the actual case, and the proportionality to temperature slope must hold.

This is exactly analogous to the replacement by a distribution on an equipotential surface of the electrical charge or charges within the surface, by a distribution over the surface, with fulfilment of Coulomb's theorem (p. 43 below) at the surface. Thomson's paper on the "Uniform Motion of Heat" gave an intuitive proof of this great theorem of electrostatics, which the statements above may help to make clear to those who have, or are willing to acquire, some elementary knowledge of electricity.

Returning to the distribution on any isothermal surface surrounding the sink (or sinks) we see that it represents a surface-sink in equilibrium with the flow in the field. The distribution on a metal shell, coinciding with the surface, which keeps the surface at a potential which is the analogue of the temperature at the isothermal surface, while the shell is under the influence of a point-charge of electricity—the analogue of the thermal source—is the distribution as affected by the induction of the point-charge. If the shell coincide with the spherical equipotential surface referred to above, and the distribution given by the theorem of replacement be made upon it, the shell will be at zero potential, and the charge will be that which would exist if the shell were uninsulated, that is, the " induced charge."

The consideration of the following simple problem will serve to make clear the meaning of an electric image, and form a suitable introduction to a description of the application of the method to the electrification of spherical surfaces. Imagine a very large plane sheet of tinfoil connected by a conducting wire with the earth.   If there are no electrified bodies near, the sheet will be unelectrified. But let a very small metallic ball with a charge of positive electricity upon it be brought moderately close to one face of the tinfoil.   The tinfoil will be electrified negatively by induction, and the distribution of the negative charge will depend on the position of the ball.   Now, it can be shown that the field of electric force, on the same side of the tinfoil as the ball, is precisely the same as would be produced if the foil (and everything behind it) were removed, and

an equal negative charge of electricity placed behind
the tinfoil on the prolonged perpendicular from the ball
to the foil, and as far from the foil behind as the ball is
from it in front. Such a negative charge behind the
tinfoil sheet is called an electric image of the positive
charge in front. It is situated, as will be seen at what
would be, if the tinfoil were a mirror, the optical
image of the ball in the mirror.

Now, suppose a second very large sheet of tinfoil to
be placed parallel to the first sheet, so that the small

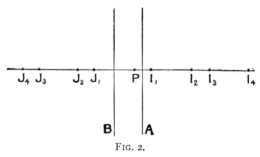

FIG. 2.

electrified sphere is between the two sheets, and that
this second sheet is also connected to the earth. The
charge on the ball induces negative electricity on both
sheets, but besides this each sheet by its charge influences the other. The problem of distribution is much
more complicated than in the case of a single sheet,
but its solution is capable of very simple statement.
Let us call the two sheets A and B (Fig. 2), and
regard them for the moment as mirrors. A first image
of an object P between the two mirrors is produced
directly by each, but the image I_1 in A is virtually an
object in front of B, and the image J_1 in B an object

in front of A, so that a second image more remote
from the mirror than the first is produced in each case.
These second images I_2 and J_2 in the same way produce third images still more remote, and so on. The
positions are determined just as for an object and a
single mirror. There is thus an infinite trail of images
behind each mirror, the places of which any one can
assign.

Every one may see the realisation of this arrangement in a shop window, the two sides of which
are covered by parallel sheets of mirror-glass. An
infinite succession of
the objects in the
window is apparently
seen on both sides.
When the objects dis-
played are glittering
new bicycles in a row
the effect is very strik-
ing; but what we
are concerned with

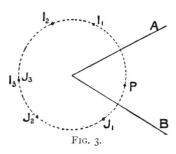

FIG. 3.

here is a single small object like the little ball, and its
two trails of images. The electric force at any point
between the two sheets of tinfoil is exactly the same
as if the sheets were removed and charges alternately
negative and positive were placed at the image-points,
negative at the first images, positive at the second
images, and so on, each charge being the same in
amount as that on the ball. We have an "electric
kaleidoscope" with parallel mirrors. When the angle
between the conducting planes is an aliquot part of
360°, let us say 60°, the electrified point and the
images are situated, just as are the object and its image

in Brewster's kaleidoscope, namely at the angular points
of a hexagon, the sides of which are alternately (as
shown in Fig. 3) of lengths twice the distance of the
electrified point from A and from B.

Now consider the spherical surface referred to at
p. 37, which is kept at uniform potential by a charge
at the external point P, and a charge q' at the inverse
point P' within the sphere. If E (Fig. 4) be any
point whatever on the surface, and r, r' be its distances
from P and P', it is easy to prove by geometry that
the two triangles CPE and CEP' are similar, and

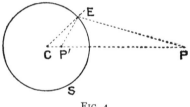

FIG. 4

therefore $r' = ra/f$. [Here a/f is used to mean a
divided by f. The mark $/$ is adopted instead of
the usual bar of the fraction, for convenience of
printing.] Now, by the explanation given above, the
potential produced at any point by a charge q at
another point, is equal to the ratio of the charge q to
the distance between the points. Thus the potential
at E due to the charge q at P is q/r, and that at E due
to a charge q' at P' is q'/r'. Thus if $q' = -qa/f$, q' at
P' will produce a potential at $E = -qa/fr' = -q/r$,
by the value of r. Hence q at P and $-qa/f$ at P'
coexisting will give potential $q/r + -q/r$, or zero,
at E. Thus the charge $-qa/f$, at the internal point

P' will in presence of $+ q$ at P keep all points of the spherical surface at zero potential. These two charges represent the source and sink in the thermal analogue of p. 37 above.

Now replace S by a spherical shell of metal connected to the earth by a long fine wire, and imagine all other conductors to be at a great distance from it. If this be under the influence of the charge q at P alone, a charge is induced upon it which, in presence of P, maintains it at zero potential. The internal charge $- qa/f$, and the induced distribution on the shell are thus equivalent as regards the potential produced by either at the spherical surface; for each counteracts then the potential produced by q at P. But it can be proved that if a distribution over an equipotential surface can be made to produce the same potential over that surface as a given internal distribution does, they produce the same potentials at all *external* points, or, as it is usually put, the external fields are the same. This is part of the statement of what has been called the "theorem of replacement" discovered by Green, Gauss, Thomson, and Chasles as described above.

Another part of the statement of the theorem may now be formulated. Coulomb showed long ago that the surface-density of electricity at any point on a conductor is proportional to the resultant field-intensity just outside the surface at that point. Since the surface is throughout at one potential this intensity is normal to the surface. Let it be denoted by N, and s be the surface-density : then according to the system of units usually adopted $4\pi s = N$.

Let now the rate of diminution of potential per unit of

distance outwards (or downward gradient of potential) from the equipotential surface be determined for every point of the surface, and let electricity be distributed over the surface, so that the amount per unit area at each point (the surface-density) is made numerically equal to the gradient there divided by 4π. This, by Coulomb's law, stated above, gives that field-intensity just outside the surface which exists for the actual distribution, and therefore, as can be proved, gives the same field everywhere else outside the surface. The external fields will therefore be equivalent, and further, the amount of electricity on the surface will be the same as that situated within it in the actual distribution.

Thus it is only necessary to find for $-qa/f$ at P' and q at P, the falling off gradient N of potential outside the spherical surface at any point E, and to take $N/4\pi$, to obtain s the surface-density at E. Calculation of this gradient for the sphere gives $4\pi s = -q(f^2 - a^2)/ar^3$. The surface-density is thus inversely as the cube of the distance PE.

If the influencing point P be situated within the spherical shell, and the shell be connected to earth as before, the induced distribution will be on its interior surface. The corresponding point P' will now be outside, but given by the same relation. And a will now be greater than f, and the density will be given by $4\pi s = -q(a^2 - f^2)/ar^3$, where f and r have the same meanings with regard to E and P as before.

P' is in each case called the image of P in the sphere S, and the charge $-qa/f$ there supposed situated is the *electric image* of the charge q at P. It will be seen that an electric image is a charge, or system of charges, on one side of an electrified surface which produces on the other side of that surface the same electrical field as is produced by the actual electrification of the surface.

While by the theorem of replacement there is only one distribution over a surface which produces at all points on one side of a surface the same field as does a distribution D on the other side of the surface, this surface distribution may be equivalent to several different arrangements of D. Thus the point-charge at P' is only one of various image-distributions equivalent to the surface-distribution in the sense explained. For example, a uniform distribution over any spherical surface with centre at P' (Fig. 4) would do as well, provided this spherical surface were not large enough to extend beyond the surface S.

In order to find the potential of the sphere (Fig. 4) when insulated with a charge Q upon it, in presence of the influencing charge q at the external point P, it is only necessary to imagine uniformly distributed over the sphere, already electrified in the manner just explained, the charge $Q + aq/f$. Then the whole charge will be Q, and the uniformity of distribution will be disturbed, as required by the action of the influencing point-charge. The potential will be $Q/a + q/f$. For a given potential V of the sphere, the total charge is $aV - aq/f$, that is the charge is aV over and above the induced charge.

If instead of a single influencing point-charge at P there be a system of influencing point-charges at different external points, each of these has an image-charge to be found in amount and situation by the method just described, and the induced distribution is that obtained by superimposing all the surface distributions found for the different influencing points.

The force of repulsion between the point-charge q and the sphere (with total charge Q) can be found at once by calculating the sum of the forces between q at P and the charges $Q + aq/f$ at C and $-aq/f$ at P'.

This can be found also by calculating the energy of the system, which will be found to consist of three terms, one representing the energy of the sphere with charge Q uninfluenced by an external charge, one representing the energy on a small conductor (not a point) at P existing alone, and a third representing the mutual energy of the electrification on the sphere and the charge q at P existing in presence of one another. By a known theorem the energy of a system of conductors is one half of the sum obtained by multiplying the potential of each conductor by its charge and adding the products together. It is only necessary then to find the variation of the last term caused by increasing f by a small amount df. This will be the product $F \cdot df$ of the force F required and the displacement.

Either method may be applied to find the forces of attraction and repulsion for the systems of electrified spheres described below.

The problem of two mutually influencing non-intersecting spheres, S_1, S_2 (Fig. 5), insulated with given charges, q_1, q_2, may now be dealt with in the following manner. Let each be supposed at first charged uniformly. By the known theorem referred to above, the external field of each is the same as if its whole charge were situated at the centre. Now if the distribution on S_2, say, be kept unaltered, while that on S_1 is allowed to change, the action of S_2 on S_1 is the same as if the charge q_2 were at the centre C_2 of S_2. Thus if f be the distance between the centres C_1, C_2, and a_1 be the radius of S_1, the distribution will be that corresponding to $q_1 + a_1 q_2 / f$ uniformly distributed on S_1, together with the induced charge $- a_1 q_2 / f$, which corresponds to the image-charge at the point I_1 (within S_1), the inverse of C_2 with respect to S_1. Now let the charge on S_1 be

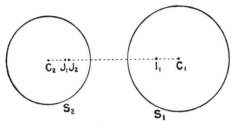

FIG. 5.

fixed in the state just supposed while that on S_2 is freed. The charge on S_2 will rearrange itself under the influence of $q_1 + a_1 q_2 / f \ (= q')$ and $- a_1 q_2 / f$, considered as at C_1 and I_1 respectively. The former of these will give a distribution equivalent to $q_2 + a_2 q' / f$ uniformly distributed over S_2, and an induced distribution of amount $- a_2 q' / f$ at J_1, the inverse point of C_1 with regard to S_2. The image-charge $- a_1 q_2 / f$ at I_1 in S_1 will react on S_2 and give an induced distribution $- a_2 (- a_1 q_2 / f) f'$, $(I_1 C_2 = f')$ corresponding to an image-charge $a_2 a_1 q_2 / f f'$ at the inverse point J_2 of P_1 with respect to $C_2 S_2$. Thus the distribution on S_2 is equivalent to $q_2 + a_2 q' / f - a_2 a_1 q_2 / f f'$ distributed uniformly over it, together with the two induced distributions just described.

In the same way these two induced distributions on S_2 may now be regarded as reacting on the distribution on S_1 as would point-charges $-a_2 q_1/f$ and $a_2 a_1 q_2/ff'$, situated at J_1 and J_2 respectively, and would give two induced distributions on S_1 corresponding to their images in S_1.

Thus by partial influences in unending succession the equilibrium state of the two spheres could be approximated to as nearly as may be desired. An infinite trail of electric images within each of the two spheres is thus obtained, and the final state of each conductor can be calculated by summation of the effects of each set of images.

If the final potentials, V_1, V_2, say, of the spheres are given the process is somewhat simpler. Let first the charges be supposed to exist uniformly distributed over each sphere, and to be of amount $a_1 V_1$, $a_2 V_2$ in the two cases. The uniform distribution on S_1 will raise the potential of S_2 above V_2, and to bring the potential down to V_2 in presence of this distribution we must place an induced distribution over S_2, represented as regards the external field by the image-charge $-a_2 a_1 V_1/f$ (at the image of C_1 in S_2) where f is the distance between the centres. The charge $a_2 V_2$ on S_2 will similarly have an action on S_1 to be compensated in the same way by an image-charge $-a_1 a_2 V_2/f$ at the image of C_2 in S_1. Now these two image-charges will react on the spheres S_1 and S_2 respectively, and will have to be balanced by induced distributions represented by second image-charges, to be found in the manner just exemplified. These will again react on the spheres and will have to be compensated as before, and so on indefinitely. The charges diminish in amount, and their positions approximate more and more, according to definite laws, and the final state is to be found by summation as before.

The force of repulsion is to be found by summing the forces between all the different pairs of charges which can be formed by taking one charge of each system at its proper point: or it can be obtained by calculating the energy of the system.

The method of successive influences was given originally by Murphy, but the mode of representing the effects of the successive induced charges by image-charges is due to Thomson. Quite another solution of this problem is, however, possible by Thomson's method of electrical inversion.

A similar process to that just explained for two charged and mutually influencing spheres will give the distribution on two concentric conducting spheres, under the influence of a point-charge q at P between the inner surface of the outer and the outer surface of the inner, as shown in Fig. 7. There the influence of q at P, and of the induced distributions on one another, is represented by two series of images, one within the inner sphere and one outside the outer. These charges and positions can be calculated from the result for a single sphere and point-charge.

Thomson's method of electrical inversion, referred to above, enabled the solutions of unsolved problems to be inferred from known solutions of simpler cases of distribution. We give here a brief account of the method, and some of its results. First we have to recall the meaning of geometrical inversion. In Fig. 6

the distances OP, OP', OQ, OQ' fulfil the relation
$OP . OP' = OQ . OQ' = a^2$.   Thus P' is (see p. 37)
the inverse of the point P with respect to a sphere of
radius a and centre O (indicated by the dotted line in
Fig. 6), and similarly Q' is the inverse of Q with
respect to the same sphere and centre. O is called the
centre of inversion, and the sphere of radius a is called
the sphere of inversion.   Thus the sphere of Figs. 1
and 4 is the sphere of inversion for the points P and
P', which are inverse points of one another.   For any
system of points P, Q, . . ., another system P', Q', . . .

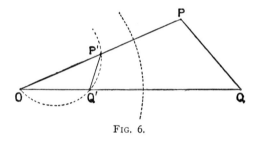

FIG. 6.

or inverse points can be found, and if the first system
form a definite locus, the second will form a derived
locus, which is called the inverse of the former.   Also
if P', Q', . . . be regarded as the direct system,
P, Q, . . . will be the corresponding inverse system
with regard to the same sphere and centre. P' is the
image of P, and P is the image of P', and so on, with
regard to the same sphere and centre of inversion.

  The inverse of a circle is another circle, and therefore the inverse of a sphere is another sphere, and the
inverse of a straight line is a circle passing through the
centre of inversion, and of an infinite plane a sphere

passing through the centre of inversion. Obviously the inverse of a sphere concentric with the sphere of inversion is a concentric sphere.

The line $P'Q'$ is of course not the inverse of the line PQ, which has for its inverse the circle passing through the three points O, P', Q', as indicated in Fig. 6.

The following results are easily proved.

A locus and its inverse cut any line OP at the same angle.

To a system of point-charges q_1, q_2, . . . at points P_1, P_2, . . . on one side of the surface of the sphere of inversion there is a system of charges aq_1/f_1, aq_2/f_2, . . . on the other side of the spherical surface $[OP_1=f_1, OP_2=f_2]$. This inverse system, as we shall call it, produces the same potential at any point of the sphere of inversion, as does the direct system from which it is derived.

If V, V' be the potentials produced by the whole direct system at Q, and by the whole inverse system at Q', $V'/V = r/a = a/r'$, where $OQ = r$, $OQ' = r'$.

Thus if V is constant over any surface S', V' is not a constant over the inverse surface S', unless r is a constant, that is, unless the surface S' is a sphere concentric with the sphere of inversion, in which case the inverse surface is concentric with it and is an equipotential surface of the inverse distribution.

Further, if q be distributed over an element dS of a surface, the inverse charge aq/f will be distributed over the corresponding element dS' of the inverse surface. But $dS'/dS = a^4/f^4 = f'^4/a^4$ where f, f' are the distances of O from dS and dS'. Thus if s be the density on dS and s' the inverse density on dS' we have $s'/s = a^3/f'^3 = f^3/a^3$.

When V is constant over the direct surface, while

r has different values for different directions of OQ, the different points of the inverse surface may be brought to zero potential by placing at O a charge $- aV$. For this will produce at Q' a potential $- aV/r'$ which with V' will give at Q' a potential zero. This shows that V' is the potential of the induced distribution on S' due to a charge $- aV$ at O, or that $- V'$ is the potential due to the induced charge on S' produced by the charge aV at O.

Thus we have the conclusion that by the process of inversion we get from a distribution in equilibrium, on

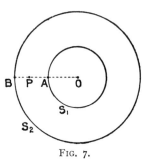

FIG. 7.

a conductor of any form, an induced distribution on the inverse surface supposed insulated and conducting ; and conversely we obtain from a given induced distribution on an insulated conducting surface, a natural equilibrium distribution on the inverse surface. In each case the inducing charge is situated at the centre of inversion. The charges on the conductor (or conductors) after inversion are always obtainable at once from the fact that they are the inverses of the charges on the conductor (or conductors) in the direct case, and the surface-densities or volume-densities can be found from the relations stated above.

Now take the case of two concentric spheres insulated and influenced by a point-charge q placed at a point P between them as shown in Fig. 7. We have seen at p. 49 how the induced distribution, and the amount of the charge, on each sphere is obtained from the two convergent series of images, one outside the outer sphere, the other inside the inner sphere. We do not here calculate the density of distribution at any point, as our object is only to explain the method ; but the quantities on the spheres S_1 and S_2, are respectively $- q \cdot OA \cdot PB / (OP \cdot AB)$, $- q \cdot OB \cdot AP / (OP \cdot AB)$.

It may be noticed that the sum of the induced charges is $- q$, and that as the radii of the spheres are both made indefinitely great, while the distance AB is kept finite, the ratios OA / OP, OB / OP approximate to unity, and the charges to $-q \cdot PB / AB$, $-q \cdot AP / AB$, that is, the charges are inversely as the distances of P from the nearest points of the two surfaces. But when the radii are made indefinitely great we have the case of two infinite plane conducting surfaces with a point-charge between them, which we have described above.

Now let this induced distribution, on the two concentric spheres, be inverted from P as centre of inversion. We obtain two non-intersecting spheres, as in Fig. 5, for the inverse geometrical system, and for the inverse electrical system an equilibrium distribution on these two spheres in presence of one another, and charged with the charges which are the inverses of the induced charges. These maintain the system of two spheres at one potential. From this inversion it is possible to proceed as shown by Maxwell in his *Electricity and Magnetism*, vol. i, § 173, to the distribution on two spheres at two different potentials; but we have shown above how the problem may be dealt with directly by the method of images.

Again take the case of two parallel infinite planes under the influence of a point-charge between them. This system inverted from P as centre gives the equilibrium distribution on two charged insulated spheres in contact (Fig. 8); for this system is the inverse of the planes and the charges upon them. Another interesting case is that of the "electric kaleidoscope" referred to above. Here the two infinite conducting planes are inclined at an angle $360°/n$, where n is a whole number, and are therefore bounded

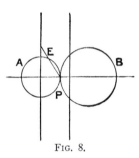

FIG. 8.

in one direction by the straight line which is their intersection. The image points I_1, J_1, . . ., of P placed in the angle between the planes are situated as shown in Fig. 3, and are $n - 1$ in number. This system inverted from P as centre gives two spherical surfaces which cut one another at the same angle as do the planes. This system is one of electrical equilibrium in free space, and therefore the problem of the distribution on two intersecting spheres is solved, for the case at least in which the angle of intersection is an aliquot part of $360°$. When the planes are at right angles the result is that for two perpendicularly intersecting planes, for which Fig. 9 gives a diagram.

But the greatest achievement of the method was the determination of the distribution on a segment of a thin spherical shell with edge in one plane. The solution of this problem was communicated to M. Liouville in the letter of date September 16, 1846,

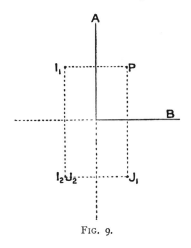

Fig. 9.

referred to above, but without proof, which Thomson stated he had not time to write out owing to preparation for the commencement of his duties as Professor of Natural Philosophy at Glasgow on November 1, 1846. It was not supplied until December 1868 and January 1869; and in the meantime the problem had not been solved by any other mathematician.

As a starting point for this investigation the distribution on a thin plane circular disk of radius a is required. This can be obtained by considering the disk

as a limiting case of an oblate ellipsoid of revolution,
charged to potential V, say.   If Fig. 10 represent the disk
and P the point at which the density is sought, so that
$CP = r$, and $CA = a$, the density is $V / \{ 2\pi^2 \sqrt{(a^2 - r^2)} \}$.

The ratio q / V, of charge to potential, which is
called the electrostatic capacity of the conductor, is
thus $2a / \pi$, that is $a / 1\cdot 571$.   It is, as Thomson notes
in his paper, very remarkable that the Hon. Henry
Cavendish should have found long ago by experiment
with the rudest apparatus the electrostatic capacity of

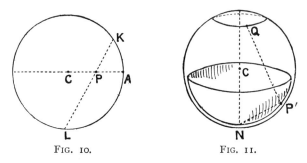

FIG. 10.   FIG. 11.

a disk to be $1 / 1\cdot 57$ of that of a sphere of the same
radius.

Now invert this disk distribution with any point Q
as centre of inversion, and with radius of inversion a.
The geometrical inverse is a segment of a spherical surface which passes through Q.   The inverse distribution
is the induced distribution on a conducting shell uninsulated and coincident with the segment, and under
the influence of a charge $- aV$ situated at Q (Fig. 11).
Call this conducting shell the "bowl."   If the surface-
densities at corresponding points on the disk and on
the inverse, say points P and P', be s and s', then, as

on page 51, $s' = sa^3 / QP'^3$. If we put in the value of s given above, that of s' can be put in a form given by Thomson, which it is important to remark is independent of the radius of the spherical surface. This expression is applicable to the other side of the bowl, inasmuch as the densities at near points on opposite sides of the plane disk are equal.

If v, v' be the potentials at any point R of space, due to the disk and to its image respectively, $-v' = av / QR$. If then R be coincident with a point P' on the spherical segment we have (since then $v = V$) $V' = aV / QP'$, which is the potential due to the induced distribution caused by the charge $-aV$ at Q as already stated.

The fact that the value of s' does not involve the radius makes it possible to suppose the radius infinite, in which case we have the solution for a circular disk uninsulated and under the influence of a charge of electricity at a point Q in the same plane but outside the bounding circle.

Now consider the two parts of the spherical surface, the bowl B, and the remainder S of the spherical surface. Q with the charge $-aV$ may be regarded as situated on the latter part of the surface. Any other influencing charges situated on S will give distributions on the bowl to be found as described above, and the resulting induced electrification can be found from these by summation. If S be uniformly electrified to density s, and held so electrified, the inducing distribution will be one given by *integration* over the whole of S, and the bowl B will be at zero potential under the influence of this electrification of S, just as if B were replaced by a shell of metal connected to the earth by a long fine wire. The densities are equal at infinitely near points on the two sides of B.

Let the bowl be a thin metal shell connected with the earth by a long thin wire and be surrounded by a concentric and complete shell of diameter f greater than that of the spherical surface, and let this shell be rigidly electrified with surface density $- s$. There will be no force within this shell due to its own electrification, and hence it will produce no change of the distribution in the interior. But the potential within will be $- 2\pi fs$, for the charge is $- \pi f^2 s$, and the capacity of the shell is $\frac{1}{2}f$. The potential of the bowl will now be zero, and its electrification will just neutralise the potential $- 2\pi fs$, that is, will be exactly the free electrification required to produce potential $2\pi fs$.

To find this electrification let the value of f be only infinitesimally greater than the diameter of the spherical surface of which B is a part; then the bowl is under the influence (1) of a uniform electrification of density $- s$ infinitely close to its outer surface, and (2) of a uniform electrification of the same density, which may be regarded as upon the surface which has been called S above. It is obvious that by (1) a density s is produced on the outer surface of the bowl, and no other effect; by (2) an equal density at infinitely near points on the opposite sides of the bowl is produced which we have seen how to calculate. Thus the distribution on the bowl freely electrified is completely determined and the density can easily be calculated. The value will be found in Thomson's paper.

Interesting results are obtained by diminishing S more and more until the shell is a complete sphere with a circular hole in it. Tabulated results for different relative dimensions of S will be found in Thomson's paper, " Reprint of Papers," Articles V, XIV, XV. Also the reader will there find full particulars of the mathematical calculations indicated in this chapter, and an extension of the method to the case of an influencing point not on the spherical surface of which the shell forms part. Further developments of the problem have been worked out by other writers, and further information with references will be found in Maxwell's *Electricity and Magnetism*, loc. cit.

It is not quite clear whether Thomson discovered *geometrical* inversion independently or not : very likely he did. His letter to Liouville of date October 8, 1845, certainly reads as if he claimed the geometrical transformation as well as the application to electricity. Liouville, however, in his Note in which he dwells on the analytical theory of the transformation says, " La transformation dont il s'agit est bien connue, du reste, et des plus simples ; c'est celle que M. Thomson lui-même a jadis employée sous le nom de principe des *images*." In Thomson and Tait's *Natural Philosophy*, § 513, the reference to the method is as follows : " Irrespectively of the special electric application, the method of images gives a remarkable kind of transformation which is often useful. It suggests for mere geometry what has been called the transformation by reciprocal radius-rectors, that is to say . . ." Then Maxwell, in his review of the " Reprint of Papers " (*Nature*, vol. vii), after referring to the fact that the solution of the problem of the spherical bowl remained undemonstrated from 1846 to 1869, says that the geometrical idea of inversion had probably been discovered and rediscovered repeatedly, but that in his opinion most of these discoveries were later than 1845, the date of Thomson's first paper.[1]

A very general method of finding the potential at any point of a region of space enclosed by a given boundary was stated by Green in his 'Essay' for the case in which the potential is known for every point of the boundary. The success of the method depends on finding a certain function, now called Green's function. When this is known the potential at any point is at once obtained by an integration over the surface. Thomson's method of images amounts to finding for the case of a region bounded by one spherical surface or more the proper value of Green's function. Green's method has been successfully employed in more complicated cases, and is now a powerful method of attack for a large range of problems in other departments of physical mathematics. Thomson only obtained a copy of Green's paper in January 1845, and probably worked out his solutions quite independently of any ideas derived from Green's general theory.

[1] The geometrical idea was, however, given and applied at least as early as 1836 by Bellavitis, for a paper entitled "Teoria delle figure inversa" appears in the *Annali delle Scienze del Regno Lombardo-Veneto* for that year. It was also described as an independent discovery by Mr. John Wm. Stubbs, in a paper in the *Philosophical Magazine* for November 1843. In a note on the history of the transformation in Taylor's *Geometry of Conics* the date (without reference) of Bellavitis is given, and it is stated that the method of inversion was given afresh by Messrs. Ingram and Stubbs (Dublin, *Phil. Soc. Trans.* I). The note also mentions that inversion was "applied by Dr. Hirst to attractions," but contains no reference to Thomson's papers!

CHAPTER V

THE CHAIR OF NATURAL PHILOSOPHY AT GLASGOW.
ESTABLISHMENT OF THE FIRST PHYSICAL
LABORATORY

THE incumbent of the Chair of Natural Philosophy in the University of Glasgow, Professor Meikleham, had been in failing health for several years, and from 1842 to 1845 his duties had been discharged by another member of the Thomson *gens*, Mr. David Thomson, B.A., of Trinity College, Cambridge, afterwards Professor of Natural Philosophy at Aberdeen. Dr. Meikleham died in May 1846, and the Faculty thereafter proceeded on the invitation of Dr. J. P. Nichol, the Professor of Astronomy, to consider whether in consequence of the great advances of physical science during the preceding quarter of a century it was not urgently necessary to remodel the arrangements for the teaching of natural philosophy in the University. The advance of science had indeed been very great. Oersted and Ampère, Henry and Faraday and Regnault, Gauss and Weber, had made discoveries and introduced quantitative ideas, which had changed the whole aspect of experimental and mathematical physics. The electrical discoveries of the time reacted on the other branches of natural philosophy, and in no small degree on mathematics itself. As a result the progress of that period has continued and has increased in rapidity, until now the accumulated results, for the most part already united in the grasp of rational theory, have gone far beyond the power of any single man to follow, much less to master.

It is interesting to look into a course of lectures such as were usually delivered in the universities a hundred years ago by the Professor of Natural Philosophy. We find a little discussion of mechanics, hydrostatics and pneumatics, a little heat, and a very little optics. Electricity and magnetism, which in our day have a literature far exceeding that of the whole of physics only sixty years ago, could hardly be said to exist. The professor of the beginning of the nineteenth century, when Lord Kelvin's predecessor was appointed, apparently found himself quite free to devote a considerable part of each lecture to reflections on the beauties of nature, and to rhetorical flights fitter for the pulpit than for the physics lecture-table.

In the intervening time the form and fashion of scientific lectures has entirely changed, and the change is a testimony to the progress of science. It is visible even in the design of the apparatus. Microscopes, for example, have a perfection and a power undreamed of by our great-grandfathers, and they are supported on stands which lack the ornamentation of that bygone time, but possess stability and convenience. Everything and everybody—even the professor, if that be possible—must be business-like ; and each moment of time must be utilised in experiments for demonstration, not for applause, and in brief and cogent statements of theory and fact. To waste time in talk that is not to the point is criminal. But withal there is need of grace of expression and vividness of description, of clearness of exposition, of imagination, even of poetical intuition : but the stern beauty of modern science is only disfigured by the old artificial adornments and irrelevancies.

This is the tone and temper of science at the present day : the task is immense, the time is short. And sixty years since some tinge of the same cast of thought was visible in scientific workers and teachers. The Faculty agreed with Dr. Nichol that there was need to bring physical teaching and equipment into line with the state of science at the time ; but they wisely decided to do nothing until they had appointed a Professor of Natural Philosophy who would be able to advise them fully and in detail. They determined, however, to make the appointment subject to such alterations in the arrangements of the department as they might afterwards find desirable.

On September 11, 1846, the Faculty met, and having considered the resolutions which had been proposed by Dr. Nichol, resolved to the effect that the appointment about to be made should not prejudice the right of the Faculty to originate or support, during the incumbency of the new professor, such changes in the arrangements for conducting instruction in physical science as it might be expedient to adopt, and that this resolution should be communicated to the candidate elected. The minute then runs : " The Faculty having deliberated on the respective qualifications of the gentlemen who have announced themselves candidates for this chair, and the vote having been taken, it carried unanimously in favour of Mr. William Thomson, B.A., Fellow of St. Peter's College, Cambridge, and formerly a student of this University, who is accordingly

declared to be duly elected : and Mr. Thomson being
within call appeared in Faculty, and the whole of
this minute having been read to him he agreed to
the resolution of Faculty above recorded and accepted
the office." It was also resolved as follows : "The
Faculty hereby prescribe Mr. Thomson an essay on
the subject, *De caloris distributione per terræ corpus*, and
resolve that his admission be on Tuesday the 13th
October, provided that he shall be found qualified by
the Meeting and shall have taken the oath and made
the subscriptions which are required by law."

At that time, and down to within the last fifteen
years, every professor, before his induction to his chair,
had to submit a Latin essay on some prescribed subject.
This was almost the last relic of the customs of the
days when university lectures were delivered in Latin,
a practice which appears to have been first broken
through by Adam Smith when Professor of Moral
Philosophy. Whatever it may have been in the
eighteenth century, the Latin essay at the end of the
nineteenth was perhaps hardly an infallible criterion of
the professor-elect's Latinity, and it was just as well to
discard it. But fifty years before, and for long after,
classical languages bulked largely in the curriculum of
every student of the Scottish Universities, and it is
undoubtedly the case that most of those who afterwards came to eminence in other departments of
learning had in their time acquitted themselves well in
the old *Litteræ Humaniores.* This was true, as we have
seen, of Thomson, and it is unlikely that the form of
his inaugural dissertation cost him much more effort
than its matter.

The subject chosen had reference no doubt to the

Professor WILLIAM THOMSON, 1846

papers on the theory of heat which Mr. Thomson had already published. The thesis was presented to the Faculty on the day appointed, and approved, and Mr. Thomson having produced a certificate of his having taken the oaths to government, and promised to subscribe the formula of the Church of Scotland as required by law, on the first convenient opportunity, " the following oath was then administered to him, which he took and subscribed : *Ego, Gulielmus Thomson, B.A., physicus professor in hac Academia designatus, promitto sancteque polliceor me in munere mihi demandato studiose fideliterque versaturum.*" Professor Thomson was then "solemnly admitted and received by all the Members present, and took his seat as a Member of Faculty."

No translation of this essay was ever published, but its substance was contained in various papers which appeared later. The following reference to it is made in an introduction attached to Article XI of his *Mathematical and Physical Papers* (vol. i, 1882).

" An application to Terrestrial Temperature, of the principle set forth in the first part of this paper relating to the age of thermal distributions, was made the subject of the author's Inaugural Dissertation on the occasion of his induction to the professorship of Natural Philosophy in the University of Glasgow, in October 1846, ' *De Motu Caloris per Terræ Corpus* '[1]: which, more fully developed afterwards, gave a very decisive limitation to the possible age of the earth as a habitation for living creatures ; and proved the untenability of the enormous claims for TIME which, uncurbed

[1] " *De Caloris distributione per Terræ Corpus* " in the Faculty minute, as stated above.

by physical science, geologists and biologists had begun to make and to regard as unchallengeable. See 'Secular Cooling of the Earth, Geological Time,' and several other Articles below." Some statement of the argument for this limitation will be given later. [See Chap. XIV.]

Thomson thus entered at the age of twenty-five on what was to be his life work as a teacher, investigator, and inventor. For he continued in office fifty-three years, so that the united tenures of his predecessor and himself amounted to only four years less than a century! He took up his duties at the opening of the college session in November, and promptly called the attention of the Faculty to the deficiencies of the equipment of apparatus, which had been allowed to fall behind the times, and required to have added to it many new instruments. A committee was appointed to consider the question and report, and as a result of the representations of this committee a sum of £100 was placed at Professor Thomson's disposal to supply his most pressing needs. In the following years repeated applications for further grants were made and various sums were voted—not amounting to more than £500 or £600 in all—which were apparently regarded as (and no doubt were, considering the times and the funds at the disposal of the Faculty) a liberal provision for the teaching of physical science. A minute of the Faculty, of date Nov. 26, 1847, is interesting.

After "emphatically deprecating" all idea that such large annual expenditure for any one department was to be regularly contemplated, the committee refer in their report to the "inadequate condition of the department in question," and express their satisfaction "with the reasonable manner in which the Professor of Natural

Philosophy has on all occasions readily modified his demands in accordance with the economical suggestions of the committee." They conclude by saying that they " view his ardour and anxiety in the prosecution of his profession with the greatest pleasure," and " heartily concur in those anticipations of his future celebrity which Monsr. Serville,[1] the French mathematician, has recently thought fit to publish to the scientific world."

Again, in April 1852, the Faculty agree to pay a sum of £137 6s. 1½d. as the price of purchases of philosophical apparatus already made, and approve of a suggestion of the committee that the expenditure on this behalf during the next year should not exceed £50, and " they desire that the purchases shall be made so far as is possible with the previously obtained concurrence of the committee." It is easy to imagine that the ardent young Professor of Natural Philosophy found the leisurely methods of his older colleagues much too slow, and in his enthusiasm anticipated consent to his demands by ordering his new instruments without waiting for committees and meetings and reports.

In an address at the opening of the Physical and Chemical Laboratories of the University College of North Wales, on February 2, 1885, Sir William Thomson (as he was then) referred to his early equipment and work as follows: " When I entered upon the professorship of Natural Philosophy at Glasgow, I found apparatus of a very old-fashioned kind. Much of it was more than a hundred years old, little of it less than fifty years old, and most of it was worm-eaten. Still, with such appliances, year

---

[1] *Sic.* Without doubt a mistake of the scribe for " Liouville."

after year, students of natural philosophy had been brought together and taught as well as possible. The principles of dynamics and electricity had been well illustrated and well taught, as well taught as lectures and so imperfect apparatus—but apparatus merely of the lecture-illustration kind—could teach. But there was absolutely no provision of any kind for experimental investigation, still less idea, even, for anything like students' practical work. Students' laboratories for physical science were not then thought of." [1]

It appears that the class of Natural Philosophy (there was then as a rule only one class in any subject, though supplementary work was done in various ways) met for systematic lectures at 9 a.m., which is the hour still adhered to, and for what was called " Experimental Physics " at 8 p.m. !

The *University Calendar* for 1863–4 states that " the Natural Philosophy Class meets two hours daily, 9 a.m. and 11 a.m. The first hour is chiefly spent in statements of Principles, description of Results of Observation, and Experimental Illustrations. The second hour is devoted to Mathematical Demonstrations and Exercises, and Examinations on all parts of the Course.

" The Text Books to be used are : ' Elements of Dynamics' (first part now ready), Printed by George Richardson, University Printer. ' Elements of Natural Philosophy,' by Professors W. Thomson and P. G. Tait (Two Treatises to be published before November. Macmillan.[2])

---

[1] *North Wales Chronicle,* Report, Feb. 7, 1885.

[2] Published : *Treatise on Natural Philosophy,* vol. i in 1867; *Elements of Natural Philosophy* in 1873.

" The shorter of the last mentioned Treatises will be used for the work required of all students of Natural Philosophy in the regular curriculum. The whole or specified parts of the larger Treatise will be prescribed in connection with voluntary examinations and exercises in the Class, and for candidates for the degree of M.A. with honours. Students who desire to undertake these higher parts of the business of the class, ought to be well prepared on all the subjects of the Senior Mathematical Class.

" The Laboratory in connection with the class is open daily from 9 a.m. to 4 p.m. for Experimental Exercises and Investigations, under the direction of the Professor and his official assistant."

In 1847 the meetings for experimental physics were changed to 11 a.m. The hour 9 a.m. is still (1908) retained for the regular meetings of the ordinary class, and 11 a.m. for meetings held twice a week for exercises and tutorial work, attendance at which is optional.

[A second graduating class has now been instituted and is very largely attended. Each student attends three lectures and spends four hours in the laboratory each week. A higher class, in two divisions, is also held.]

At an early date in his career as a professor Thomson called in the aid of his students for experimental research. In many directions the properties of matter still lay unexplored, and it was necessary to obtain exact data for the perfecting of the theories of elasticity, electricity and heat, which had been based on the researches of the first half of the nineteenth century. To the authors of these theories—Gauss, Green, Cauchy and others—he was a fit successor. Not knowing all that had been done by these men of genius, he reinvented, as we have seen, some of their great theorems, and in somewhat later work, notably in electricity and magnetism, set the theories on a new basis cleared of all extraneous and unnecessary matter, and reduced the hypotheses and assumptions to the smallest possible number, stated with the most careful precautions against misunderstanding. As this work was gradually accomplished the need for further experiment became more and more clearly apparent. Accordingly he established at the old College in the High Street, what he has justly claimed was the first physical laboratory for students.[1] An old wine-cellar in the basement adjoining the Natural Philosophy Class-room was first annexed, and was the scene of early researches, which were to lead to much of the best work of the present time. To this was added a little later the Blackstone Examination-room, which, disused and "left unprotected," was added to the wine-cellar, and gave space for the increasing corps of enthusiastic workers who came under the influence of the new teacher, and were eager to be associated with his work. A good many of the researches which were carried out in this meagre accommodation in the old College will be mentioned in what follows.

[In the view of the inner court of the Old College given opposite, the windows on the ground-floor to

---

[1] The exact date at which this was done cannot be determined from the Minutes of the Faculty, as they contain no reference to the appropriation of space for the purpose. In his *Oration on James Watt*, delivered at the Ninth Jubilee of the University of Glasgow, in 1901, Lord Kelvin referred to the Glasgow Physical Laboratory as having grown up between 1846 and 1856 ; and elsewhere he has referred to it as having been "incipient" in 1851.

INNER COURT OF THE OLD COLLEGE
Showing Natural Philosophy Rooms

the right of the turret in front, are those of the Blackstone Examination-room, which formed a large part
of the new Physical Laboratory. The windows above
these, on the second floor, are those of the Apparatus-
room of the Natural Philosophy Department. Between
the turret on the right of the picture and the angle of
the court are the windows of the Natural Philosophy
Class-room. The attic above the Apparatus-room
was at a later time occupied by the Engineering
Department, under Professor Macquorn Rankine.]

Here again we may quote from the Bangor address :

" Soon after I entered my present chair in the
University of Glasgow in 1846 I had occasion to
undertake some investigations of electrodynamic
qualities of matter, to answer questions suggested by
the results of mathematical theory, questions which
could only be answered by direct experiment. The
labour of observing proved too heavy, much of it
could scarcely be carried on without two or more
persons working together. I therefore invited students
to aid in the work. They willingly accepted the
invitation, and lent me most cheerful and able help.
Soon after, other students, hearing that their class-
fellows had got experimental work to do, came to me
and volunteered to assist in the investigation. I could
not give them all work in the particular investigation
with which I had commenced—'the electric convection of heat'—for want of means and time and
possibilities of arrangement, but I did all in my power
to find work for them on allied subjects (Electrodynamic Properties of Metals, Moduluses of Elasticity
of Metals, Elastic Fatigue, Atmospheric Electricity,
etc.). I then had an ordinary class of a hundred

students, of whom some attended lectures in natural philosophy two hours a day, and had nothing more to do from morning till night. These were the palmy days of natural philosophy in the University of Glasgow—the pre-Commissional days. But the majority of the class really had very hard work, and many of them worked after class-hours for self-support. Some were engaged in teaching, some were city-missionaries, intending to go into the Established Church of Scotland or some other religious denomination of Scotland, or some of the denominations of Wales, for I always had many Welsh students. In those days, as now, in the Scottish Universities all intending theological students took a 'philosophical curriculum'—'zuerst collegium logicum,' then moral philosophy, and (generally last) natural philosophy. Three-fourths of my volunteer experimentalists used to be students who entered the theological classes immediately after the completion of the philosophical curriculum. I well remember the surprise of a great German professor when he heard of this rule and usage : 'What ! do the theologians learn physics ?' I said, 'Yes, they all do ; and many of them have made capital experiments. I believe they do not find that their theology suffers at all from (their) having learned something of mathematics and dynamics and experimental physics before they enter upon it.'"

This statement, besides throwing an interesting light on the conditions of university work sixty years ago, gives an illustration of the wide interpretation in Scotland of the term *Arts*. Here it has meant, since the Chair of Natural Philosophy was founded in 1577, and held by one of the Regents of the University, *Artes Liberales* in the widest sense, that is, the study of *Litteræ Humaniores* (including mental and moral philosophy) and physical and mathematical science. These were all deemed necessary for a liberal education at that time : in the scientific age in which we live it is more imperative than ever that neither should be excluded from the Arts curriculum of our Universities. The common distinction between Arts and Science is a false one, and the product of a narrow idea which is alien to the traditions of our northern Universities.

It is to be noted, however, that the laboratory thus founded was essentially a research laboratory ; it was not designed for the systematic instruction of students in methods of experimenting. Laboratories for this purpose came later, and as a natural consequence. But for the best students, ill prepared as, no doubt, some of them were for the work of research, the experience gained in such a laboratory was very valuable. They learned—and, indeed, had to learn—in an incidental manner how to determine physical constants, such as specific gravities, thermal capacities, electric resistances, and so forth. For, apart from the *Relations des Expériences* of Regnault, and the magnetic and electric work of Gauss and Weber, there was no systematised body of information available for the guidance of students. Good students could branch out from the main line of inquiry, so as to acquire skill in subsidiary determinations of this kind ; to the more easily daunted student such difficulties proved formidable, and often absolutely deterrent.

It is not easy for a physicist of the present day to realise the state of knowledge of the time, and so he often fails to recognise the full importance of

Thomson's work. The want of precise knowledge of physical constants was to a considerable extent a consequence of the want of exact definitions of quantities to be determined, and in a much greater degree of the lack of any system of units of measurement. The study of phenomena was in the main merely qualitative ; where an attempt had been made to obtain quantitative determinations, the units employed were arbitrary and dependent on apparatus in the possession of the experimenter, and therefore unavailable to others. In the department of heat, as has been said, a great beginning had been made by Regnault, in whose hands the exact determination of physical constants had become a fine art.

In electricity and magnetism there were already the rudiments of quantitative measurement. But it was only long after, when the actions of magnets and of electric currents had been much further studied, that the British Association entered on its great work of setting up a system of absolute units for the measurement of such actions. Up till then the resistance, for example, of a piece of wire, to the passage of an electric current along it, was expressed by some such specification as that it was equal to the resistance of a certain piece of copper wire in the experimenter's possession. It was therefore practically impossible for experimenters elsewhere to profit by the information. And so in other cases. An example from Thomson's papers on the " Dynamical Theory of Heat " may be cited here, though it refers to a time (1851) when some progress towards obtaining a system of absolute units had been made. In § 118 (Art. XLVIII) he states that the electromotive force of a thermoelectric couple of copper and bismuth, at temperatures 0° C. and 100° C. of its functions, might be estimated from a comparison made by Pouillet of the strength of the current sent by this electromotive force through a copper wire 20 metres long and 1 millimetre in diameter, with the strength of a current decomposing water at a certain rate, were it not that the specific resistances of different specimens of copper are found to differ considerably from one another. Hence, though an estimate is made, it is stated that, without experiments on the actual wire used by Pouillet, it was impossible to arrive at an accurate result. Now if it had been in Pouillet's power to determine accurately the resistance of his circuit in absolute units, there would have been no difficulty in the matter, and his result would have been immediately available for the estimate required.

When submarine cables came to be manufactured and laid all this had to be changed. For they were expensive ; an Atlantic cable, for example, cost half a million sterling. The state of the cable had to be ascertained at short intervals during manufacture ; a similar watch had to be kept upon it during the process of laying, and afterwards during its life of telegraphic use. The observations made by one observer had therefore to be made available to all, so that, with other instruments and at another place, equivalent observations could be made and their results quantitatively compared with those of the former. To set up a system of measurement for such purposes as these involved much theoretical discussion and an enormous amount of experimental investigation. This was undertaken by a special committee of the Association, and a principal part in furnishing discussions of theory and in devising experimental methods was taken by Thomson. The committee's investigations took place at a date somewhat later in Thomson's career than that with which we are here dealing, and some account of them will be given in a later chapter; but much work, preparatory for and leading up to the determination of electrical standards, was done by the volunteer laboratory corps in the transformed wine-cellar of the old College.

The selection and realisation of electrical standards was a work of extraordinary importance to the world from every point of view—political, commercial, and social. It not only rendered applications of electricity possible in the arts and industries, but by relieving experimental results from the vagueness of the specifications formerly in use, made the further progress of pure electrical science a matter in which every step forward, taken by an individual worker, facilitated the advance of all. But like other toilsome services, the nature of which is not clear to the general public, it has never received proper acknowledgment from those who have profited by it. If Thomson had done nothing more than the work he did in this connection, first with his students and later with the British Association Committee, he would have deserved well of his fellow-countrymen.

When Professor Thomson was entering on the duties of his chair, and calling his students to his aid, the discoveries of Faraday on the induction of currents by the motion of magnets in the neighbourhood of closed circuits of wire, or, what comes to the same thing, the motion of such circuits in the "fields" of magnets, had not been long given to the world, and were being pondered deeply by natural philosophers. The time was ripe for a quantitative investigation of current induction, like that furnished by the genius of Ampère after the discovery by Oersted of the deflection of a magnet by an electric current. Such an investigation was immensely facilitated by Faraday's conception of lines of magnetic force, the cutting of which by the wire of the circuit gave rise to the induced current. Indeed, the mathematical ideas involved were indicated, and not obscurely, by Faraday himself. But to render the mathematical theory explicit, and to investigate and test its consequences, required the highest genius. This work was accomplished in great measure by Thomson, whose presentation of electrodynamic theory helped Maxwell to the view that light was an affair of the propagation of electric and magnetic vibrations in an insulating medium, the light-carrying ether.

Another investigation on which he had already entered in 1847 was of great importance, not only for pure science but for the development and proper economy of all industrial operations. The foundations on which a dynamical theory of heat was to be raised had been partly laid by Carnot and were being completed on the experimental side by James Prescott Joule, whom Thomson met in 1847 at the meeting of the British Association at Oxford. The meeting at Oxford in 1860 is memorable to the public at large, mainly on account of the discussion which took place on the Darwinian theory, and the famous dialectic encounter between Bishop Wilberforce and Professor Huxley ; the Oxford meeting of 1894 will always be associated with the announcement of the discovery of argon by Lord Rayleigh and Sir William Ramsay : the meeting of 1847 might quite as worthily be remembered as that at which Joule laid down, with numerical exactitude, the first law of thermodynamics. Joule brought his experimental results before the Mathematical and Physical Section at that meeting ; and it appears probable that they would have received scant attention had not their importance been forcibly pointed out by Thomson. Communications thereafter passed frequently between the two young physicists, and there soon began a collaboration of great value to science, and a friendship which lasted till the death of Joule in 1884. [See p. 88 below.]

We shall devote the next few chapters to an account, as free from technicalities as possible, of these great divisions of Thomson's earlier original work as professor at Glasgow.

CHAPTER VI

DURING his residence at Cambridge Thomson gained
the friendship of George Gabriel Stokes, who had
graduated as Senior Wrangler and First Smith's
Prizeman in 1841. They discussed mathematical
questions together and contributed articles on various
topics to the *Cambridge Mathematical Journal*. In
1846 " Cambridge and Dublin " was substituted for
" Cambridge " in the title of the *Journal*, and a new
series was begun under the editorship of Thomson.
A feature of the earlier volumes of the new issue was a
series of Notes on Hydrodynamics written by agreement between Thomson and Stokes, and printed in
vols. ii, iii, and v. The first, second, and fifth of
the series were written by Thomson, the others by
Stokes. The matter of these Notes was not altogether
novel; but many points were put in a new and more
truly physical light, and the series was no doubt of
much service to students, for whose use the articles
were intended. Some account of these Notes will be
given in a later chapter on Thomson's hydrodynamical
papers.

For the mathematical power and sure physical
instinct of Stokes Thomson had always the greatest
admiration. When asked on one occasion who was

the most outstanding worker in physical science on the continent, he replied, "I do not know, but whoever he is, I am certain that Stokes is a match for him." In a report of an address which he delivered in June 1897, at the celebration of the Jubilee of Sir George Stokes as Lucasian Professor of Mathematics, Lord Kelvin referred to their early intercourse at Cambridge in terms which were reported as follows: "When he reflected on his own early progress, he was led to recall the great kindness shown to himself, and the great value which his intercourse with Sir George Stokes had been to him through life. Whenever a mathematical difficulty occurred he used to say to himself, 'Ask Stokes what he thinks of it.' He got an answer if answer was possible ; he was told, at all events, if it was unanswerable. He felt that in his undergraduate days, and he felt it more now."

After the death of Stokes in February 1902, Lord Kelvin again referred, in an enthusiastic tribute in *Nature* for February 12, to these early discussions. "Stokes's scientific work and scientific thought is but partially represented by his published writings. He gave generously and freely of his treasures to all who were fortunate enough to have an opportunity of receiving from him. His teaching me the principles of solar and stellar chemistry when we were walking about among the colleges sometime prior to 1852 (when I vacated my Peterhouse Fellowship to be no more in Cambridge for many years) is but one example."

The interchange of ideas between Stokes and Thomson which began in those early days went on constantly and seems to have been stimulating to both.

The two men were in a sense complementary in nature and temperament. Both had great power and great insight, but while Stokes was uniformly calm, reflective, and judicial, Thomson's enthusiasm was more outspokenly fervid, and he was apt to be at times vehement and impetuous in his eagerness to push on an investigation ; and though, as became his nationality, he was cautious in committing himself to conclusions, he exercised perhaps less reserve in placing his results before the public of science.

A characteristic instance of Thomson's vehement pursuit of experimental results may be given here, although the incidents occurred at a much later date in his career than that with which we are at present concerned. In 1880 the invention of the Faure Secondary Battery attracted his attention. M. Faure brought from Paris some cells made up and ready charged, and showed in the Physical Laboratory at Glasgow the very powerful currents which, in consequence of their very low internal resistance, they were capable of producing in a thick piece of copper wire. The cells were of the original form, constructed by coating strips of sheet lead on both sides with a paste of minium moistened with dilute sulphuric acid, swathing them in woollen cloth sewed round them, and then rolling two together to form the pair of plates for one cell.

A supply of sheet lead, minium, and woollen cloth was at once obtained, and the whole laboratory corps of students and staff was set to work to manufacture secondary batteries. A small Siemens-Halske dynamo was telegraphed for to charge the cells, and the ventilating steam-engine of the University was requisitioned

to drive the dynamo during the night. Thus the
University stokers and engineer were put on double
shifts ; the cells were charged during the night and the
charging current and battery-potential measured at
intervals.

Then the cells were run down during the day, and
their output measured in the same way. Just as this
began, Thomson was laid up with an ailment which
confined him to bed for a couple of weeks or so ; but
this led to no cessation of the laboratory activity.   On
the contrary, the laboratory corps was divided into two
squads, one for the night, the other for the day, and the
work of charging and discharging, and of measurement
of expenditure and return of energy went on without
intermission.   The results obtained during the day
were taken to Thomson's bedside in the evening, and
early in the morning he was ready to review those
which had been obtained during the night, and to suggest further questions to be answered without delay.
This mode of working could not go on indefinitely, but
it continued until his assistants (some of whom had to
take both shifts !), to say nothing of the stokers and
students, were fairly well exhausted.

On other occasions, when he was from home, he
found the post too slow to convey his directions to his
laboratory workers, and telegraphed from day to day
questions and instructions regarding the work on hand.
Thus one important result (anticipated, however, by
Villari) of the series of researches on the effects of
stress on magnetisation which forms Part VII of his
Electrodynamic Qualities of Metals—the fact that up
to a certain magnetising force the effect of pull,
applied to a wire of soft iron, is to increase the

magnetisation produced, and for higher magnetising forces to diminish it—was telegraphed to him on the night on which the paper was read to the Royal Society.

It will thus be seen that Thomson, whether confined to his room or on holiday, kept his mind fixed upon his scientific or practical work, and was almost impatient for its progress. Stokes worked mainly by himself; but even if he had had a corps of workers and assistants, it is improbable that such disturbances of hours of attendance and laboratory and workshop routine would have occurred, as were not infrequent at Glasgow when Thomson's work was, in the 'sixties and 'seventies, at its intensest.

Stokes and Thomson were in succession presidents of the Royal Society, Stokes from 1885 to 1890, and Thomson (from 1892 as Lord Kelvin) from 1890 to 1895. This is the highest distinction which any scientific man in this country can achieve, and it is very remarkable that there should have been in recent times two presidents in succession whose modes of thought and mathematical power are so directly comparable with those of the great founder of modern natural philosophy. Stokes had the additional distinction of being the lineal successor of Newton as Lucasian Professor of Mathematics at Cambridge. But it was reserved for Thomson to do much by the publication of Thomson and Tait's *Natural Philosophy* to bring back the current of teaching and thought in dynamical science to the ideas of the *Principia*, and to show how completely the fundamental laws, as laid down in that great classic, avail for the inclusion of the modern theory of energy, in all its transformations, within the category of dynamical action between material systems.

An exceedingly eminent politician, now deceased, said some years ago that the present age was singularly deficient in minds of the first quality. So far as scientific genius is concerned, the dictum was singularly false : we have here a striking proof of the contrary. But then few politicians know anything of science ; indeed some of those who guide, or aspire to guide, the destinies of the most scientific and industrial empire the world has ever seen are almost boastful of their ignorance. There are, of course, honourable exceptions.

It is convenient to refer here to the share which Stokes and Thomson took in the physical explanation of the dark lines of the solar spectrum, and to their prediction of the possibility of determining the con- stitution of the stars and of terrestrial substances by what is now known as spectrum analysis. Thomson used to give the physical theory of these lines in his lectures, and say that he obtained the idea from Stokes in a conversation which they had in the garden of Pembroke at Cambridge, " some time prior to 1852 " (see the quotation from his *Nature* article quoted above, p. 80, and the *Baltimore Lectures*, p. 101). This is confirmed by a student's note-book, of date 1854, which is now in the Natural Philosophy Department. The statements therein recorded are perfectly definite and clear, and show that at that early date the whole affair of spectrum analysis was in his hands, and only required confirmation by experiments on the reversal of the lines of terrestrial substances by an atmosphere of the substance which produced the lines, and a comparison of the positions of the bright lines of terrestrial substances with those of the dark lines of the solar spectrum. Why Thomson did not carry out all these experiments it would be difficult to say. Some of them he did make, for Professor John Ferguson, who was a student of Natural Philosophy in 1859–60, has recently told how he witnessed Thomson make the experiment of reversing the lines of sodium by passing the light from the salted flame of a spirit lamp through vapour of sodium produced by heating the metal in an iron spoon. A few days later, says Professor Ferguson, Thomson read a letter to his class announcing Bunsen and Kirchhoff's discovery.

A letter of Stokes to Sir John Lubbock, printed in the *Scientific Correspondence of Sir George Gabriel Stokes*, states his recollection of the matter, and gives Thomson the credit of having inferred the method of spectrum analysis, a method to which Stokes himself makes no claim. He says, " I know, I think, what Sir William Thomson was alluding to. I knew well, what was generally known, and is mentioned by Herschel in his treatise on Light, that the bright D seen in flames is specially produced when a salt of soda is introduced. I connected it in my own mind with the presence of sodium, and I suppose others did so too. The coincidence in position of the bright and dark D is too striking to allow us to regard it as fortuitous. In conversation with Thomson I explained the connection of the dark and bright line by the analogy of a set of piano strings tuned to the same note, which, if struck, would give out that note, and also would be ready to sound it, to take it up, in fact, if it were sounded in air. This would imply absorption of the aërial vibrations, as otherwise there would be a creation of energy. Accordingly I accounted for the presence of the dark D in the solar spectrum by supposing that there was sodium in the atmosphere, capable of absorbing light of that particular refrangibility. He asked me if there were any other instances of such coincidences of bright and dark lines, and I said I thought there was one mentioned by Brewster. He was much struck with this, and jumped to the conclusion that to find out what substances were in the stars we must compare the positions of the dark lines seen in their spectra with the spectra of metals, etc. . . .

"I should have said that I thought Thomson was going too fast ahead, for my notion at the time was that, though a few of the dark lines might be traced to elementary substances, sodium for one, probably potassium for another, yet the great bulk of them were probably due to compound vapours, which, like peroxide of nitrogen and some other known compound gases, have the character of selective absorption."

It will be remembered that the experimental establishment of the method of spectrum analysis was published towards the end of 1859 by Bunsen and Kirchhoff, to whom, therefore, the full credit of discoverers must be given.

Lord Kelvin in the later years of his life used to tell the story of his first meeting with Joule at Oxford, and of their second meeting a fortnight later in Switzerland. He did so also in his address delivered on the occasion of the unveiling of a statue of Joule, in Manchester Town Hall, on December 7, 1893, and we quote the narrative on account of its scientific and personal interest. "I can never forget the British

Association at Oxford in 1847, when in one of the sections I heard a paper read by a very unassuming young man, who betrayed no consciousness in his manner that he had a great idea to unfold. I was tremendously struck with the paper. I at first thought it could not be true, because it was different from Carnot's theory, and immediately after the reading of the paper I had a few words with the author, James Joule, which was the beginning of our forty years' acquaintance and friendship. On the evening of the same day, that very valuable institution of the British Association, its conversazione, gave us opportunity for a good hour's talk and discussion over all that either of us knew of thermodynamics. I gained ideas which had never entered my mind before, and I thought I, too, suggested something worthy of Joule's consideration when I told him of Carnot's theory. Then and there in the Radcliffe Library, Oxford, we parted, both of us, I am sure, feeling that we had much more to say to one another and much matter for reflection in what we had talked over that evening. But . . . a fortnight later, when walking down the valley of Chamounix, I saw in the distance a young man walking up the road towards me, and carrying in his hand something which looked like a stick, but which he was using neither as an alpenstock nor as a walking-stick. It was Joule with a long thermometer in his hand, which he would not trust by itself in the *char-à-banc*, coming slowly up the hill behind him, lest it should get broken. But there, comfortably and safely seated in the *char-à-banc*, was his bride—the sympathetic companion and sharer in his work of after years. He had not told me in Section A, or in the

Radcliffe Library, that he was going to be married in three days, but now in the valley of Chamounix he introduced me to his young wife. We appointed to meet again a fortnight later at Martigny to make experiments on the heat of a waterfall (Sallanches) with that thermometer : and afterwards we met again and again, and from that time, indeed, remained close friends till the end of Joule's life. I had the great pleasure and satisfaction for many years, beginning just forty years ago, of making experiments along with Joule which led to some important results in respect to the theory of thermodynamics. This is one of the most valuable recollections of my life, and is indeed as valuable a recollection as I can conceive in the possession of any man interested in science."

At the beginning of his course of lectures each session, Professor Thomson read, or rather attempted to read, an introductory address on the scope and methods of physical science, which he had prepared for his first session in 1846. It set forth the fact that in science there were two stages of progress—a natural history stage and a natural philosophy stage. In the first the discoverer or teacher is occupied with the collection of facts, and their arrangement in classes according to their nature ; in the second he is concerned with the relations of facts already discovered and classified, and endeavours to bring them within the scope of general principles or causes. Once the philosophical stage is reached, its methods and results are connected and enlarged by continued research after facts, controlled and directed by the conclusions of general theory. Thus the method is at first purely inductive, but becomes in the second stage both

inductive and deductive ; the general theory predicts by
its deductions, and the verification of these by experiment and observation give a validity to the theory
which no mere induction could afford. These stages
of scientific investigation are well illustrated by the
laws of Kepler arrived at by mere comparison of the
motions of the planets, and the deduction of these
laws, with the remarkable correction of the third law,
given by the theory of universal gravitation. The
prediction of the existence and place of the planet
Neptune from the perturbations of Uranus is an
excellent example of the predictive quality of a true
philosophical theory.

The lecture then proceeded to state the province of
dynamics, to define its different parts, and to insist on
the importance of kinematics, which was described as
a purely geometrical subject, the geometry of motion,
considerations from which entered into every dynamical
problem. This distinction between dynamical and
kinematical considerations—between those in which
force is concerned and those into which enter only
the idea of displacement in space and in time—is
emphasised in Thomson and Tait's *Natural Philosophy*,
which commences with a long chapter devoted entirely
to kinematics.

Whether Professor Thomson read the whole of the
Introductory Lecture on the first occasion is uncertain
—Clerk Maxwell is said to have asserted that it was
closely adhered to, for that one time only, and finished
in much less than the hour allotted to it. In later
years he had never read more than a couple of pages
when some new illustration, or new fact of science,
which bore on his subject, led him to digress from the

manuscript, which was hardly ever returned to, and after a few minutes was mechanically laid aside and forgotten. Once on beginning the session he humorously informed the assembled class that he did not think he had ever succeeded in reading the lecture through before, and added that he had determined that they should hear the whole of it ! But again occurred the inevitable digression, in the professor's absorption in the new topic the promise was forgotten, and the written lecture fared as before ! These digressions were exceedingly interesting to the best students : whether they compensated for the want of a carefully prepared presentation of the elements of the subject, suited to the wants of the mass of the members of the class, is a matter which need not here be discussed. All through his elementary lectures—introductory or not—new ideas and new problems continually presented themselves. An eminent physicist once remarked that Thomson was perhaps the only living man who made discoveries while lecturing. That was hardly true ; in the glow of action and stress of expression the mind of every intense thinker often sees new relations, and finds new points of view, which amount to discoveries. But fecundity of mind has, of course, its disadvantages : the unexpected cannot happen without causing distractions to all concerned. A mind which can see a theory of the physical universe in a smoke-ring is likely, unless kept under extraordinary and hampering restraint, to be tempted to digress from what is strictly the subject in hand, to the world of matters which that subject suggests. Professor Thomson was, it must be admitted, too discursive for the ordinary student, and perhaps did not study the art of boiling down physical theories to the form most easily digestible. His eagerness of mind and width of mental outlook gave his lectures a special value to the advanced student, so that there was a compensating advantage.

The teacher of natural philosophy is really placed in a position of extraordinary difficulty. The fabric of nature is woven without seam, and to take it to pieces is in a manner to destroy it. It must, after examination in detail, be reconstructed and considered as a whole, or its meaning escapes us. And here lies the difficulty : every bit of matter stands in relation to everything else, and both sides of every relation must be considered. In other words, in the explanation of any one phenomenon the explanation of all others is more or less involved. This does not mean that investigation or exposition is impossible, or that we cannot proceed step by step ; but it shows the foolishness of that criticism of science and scientific method which asks for complete or ultimate knowledge, and of the popular demand for a simple form of words to express what is in reality infinitely complex.

In the earlier years of his professorship Professor Thomson taught his class entirely himself, and gathered round him, as he has told us in the Bangor address, an enthusiastic band of workers who aided him in the researches which he began on the electrodynamic qualities of metals, the elastic properties of substances, the thermal and electrical conductivities of metals, and at a later date in the electric and magnetic work which he undertook as a member of the British Association Committee on Electrical Standards. The class met, as has been stated, twice a day, first for lectures, then for exercises and oral examination. The changes which took place later in the curriculum, and especially the introduction of honours classes in the different subjects, rendered it difficult, if not impossible, for two hours' attendance to be given daily on all subjects, and students were at first excused attendance at the second hour, and finally such attendance became practically optional. But so long as the old traditional curriculum in Arts—of Humanity, Greek, Logic, Mathematics, Moral Philosophy and Natural Philosophy—endured, a large number of students found it profitable to attend at both hours, and it was possible to give a large amount of excellent tutorial instruction by the working of examples and oral examination.

Thomson always held that his commission included the subject of physical astronomy, and though his lectures on that subject were, as a rule, confined to a statement of Kepler's laws and Newton's deductions from them, he took care that the written and oral examinations included astronomical questions, for which the students were enjoined to prepare by reading Herschel's *Outlines*, or some similar text-book. This injunction not infrequently was disregarded, and discomfiture of the student followed as a matter of course, if he was called on to answer. Nor were the questions always easy to prepare for by reading. A man might have a fair knowledge of elementary astronomy, and be unable to answer offhand such a question as, "Why is the ecliptic called the ecliptic ? " or to say, when the lectures on Kepler had been omitted, short and tersely just what was Newton's deduction from the third law of the planetary motions.

Home exercises were not prescribed as part of the

regular work except from time to time in the "Higher Mathematical Class" which for thirty years or more of Thomson's tenure of office was held in the department. But the whole ordinary class met every Monday morning and spent the usual lecture hour in answering a paper of dynamical and physical questions. As many as ten, and sometimes eleven, questions were set in these papers, some of them fairly difficult and involving novel ideas, and by this weekly paper of problems the best students, a dozen or more perhaps, were helped to acquire a faculty of prompt and brief expression. It was not uncommon for a good man to score 80 or 90 or even 100 per cent. in the paper, no small feat to accomplish in a single hour. But to a considerable majority of the class, it is doubtful whether the weekly examination was of much advantage: they attempted one or two of the more descriptive questions perhaps, but a good many did next to nothing. The examinations came every week, and so the preparation for one after another was neglected, and as much procrastination of work ensued as there would have been if only four or five papers a session had been prescribed. Then the work of looking over so many papers was a heavy task to the professor's assistant, a task which became impossible when, for a few years in the early 'eighties, the students in the ordinary class numbered about 250.

The subject of natural philosophy had become so extensive in 1846 that Professor J. P. Nichol called attention to the necessity for special arrangements for its adequate teaching. What would he say if he could survey its dimensions at the present time ! To give even a brief outline of the principal topics in dynamics,

heat, acoustics, light, magnetism, and electricity is more
than can be accomplished in any course of university
lectures ; and the only way to teach well and economic-
ally the large numbers of students [1] who now throng
the physics classes is to give each week, say, three
lectures as well considered and arranged as possible,
without any interruption from oral examination, and
assemble the students in smaller classes two or three
times a week for exercises and oral examination.

Thomson stated his views as to examinations and
lectures in the Bangor address. "The object of a
university is teaching, not testing, . . . in respect to
the teaching of a university the object of examination is to promote the teaching. The examination
should be, in the first place, daily. No professor should
meet his class without talking to them. He should
talk to them and they to him. The French call a
lecture a *conférence*, and I admire that idea. Every
lecture should be a conference of teachers and students.
It is the true ideal of a professorial lecture. I have
found that many students are afflicted when they
come up to college with the disease called 'aphasia.'
They will not answer when questioned, even when
the very words of the answer are put in their mouths,
or when the answer is simply ' yes ' or ' no.' That
disease wears off in a few weeks, but the great cure
for it is in repeated and careful and very free interchange of question and answer between teacher and
student. . . . Written examinations are very important, as training the student to express with

[1] There are now in Glasgow in the winter session alone about 360
elementary students and 80 advanced students, and about 250 taking
practical laboratory work.

clearness and accuracy the knowledge he has gained, but they should be once a week to be beneficial."

The great difficulty now, when both classes and subject have grown enormously, is to have free conversation between professor and student, and yet give an adequate account of the subject. To examine orally in a thorough way two students in each class-hour is about as much as can be done if there is to be any systematic exposition by lecture at all; and thus the conference between teacher and individual student can occur only twice a year at most. Nevertheless Lord Kelvin was undoubtedly right : oral examination and the training of individual students in the art of clear and ready expression are very desirable. The real difficulties of the subject are those which occur to the best students, and a discussion of them in the presence of others is good for all. This is difficult nowadays, for large classes cannot afford to wait while two or three backward students grope after answers to questions—which in many cases must be on points which are sufficiently plain to the majority—to say nothing of the temptation to disorder which the display of personal peculiarities or oddities of expression generally affords to an assembly of students. But time will be economised and many advantages added, if large classes are split up into sections for tutorial work, to supplement the careful presentation of the subject made in the systematic lectures delivered to the whole class in each case. The introduction of a tutorial system will, however, do far more harm than good, unless the method of instruction is such as to foster the self-reliance of the student, who must not be, so to speak, spoon-fed : such a method, and the advantages of the weekly examination on paper may be secured, by setting the tutorial class to work out on the spot exercises prescribed by the lecturer. But the danger, which is a very real one, can only be fully avoided by the precautions of a skilful teacher, who in those small classes will draw out and direct the ideas of his students, rather than impart knowledge directly.

After a few years Thomson found it necessary to appoint an assistant, and Mr. Donald McFarlane, who had distinguished himself in the Mathematics and Natural Philosophy classes, was chosen. Mr. McFarlane was originally a block-printer, and seems to have been an apprentice at Alexandria in the Vale of Leven, at the time of the passing of the first Reform Bill. After some time spent in the cotton industry of the district, he became a teacher in a village school in the Vale of Leven, and afterwards entered the University as a student. He discharged his duties in the most faithful and self-abnegating manner until his retirement in 1880, when he had become advanced in years. He had charge of the instruments of the department, got ready the lecture illustrations and attended during lecture to assist in the experiments and supply numerical data when required, prepared the weekly class examination paper and read the answers handed in, and assisted in the original investigations which the professor was always enthusiastically pursuing. A kind of universal physical genius was McFarlane; an expert calculator and an exact and careful experimentalist. Many a long and involved arithmetical research he carried out, much apparatus he made in a homely way, and much he repaired and adjusted. Then, always when the professor was out of the way and calm had descended on the apparatus-room, if not on the laboratory, McFarlane sat down to reduce his pile of examination papers, lest Monday should arrive with a new deluge of crude answers and queer mistakes, ere the former had disappeared. On Friday afternoons at 3 o'clock he gave solutions of the previous Monday's questions to any members of the class who cared to attend ; and his clear and deliberate explanations were much appreciated. An unfailing tribute was rendered to him every year by the students, and often took the form of a valuable gift for which one and all had subscribed. A recluse he was in his way, hardly anybody knew where he lived—the professor certainly did not—and a man of the highest ability and of the most absolute unselfishness. An hour in the evening with one or two special friends, and the study of German, were the only recreations of McFarlane's solitary life. He was full of humour, and told with keen enjoyment stories of the University worthies of a by-gone age. For thirty years he worked on for a meagre salary, for during the earlier part of that time no provision for assistants was made in the Government grant to the Scottish Universities. By an ordinance issued in 1861 by the University Commissioners, appointed under the Act of 1858, a grant of £100 a year was made from the Consolidated Fund for an assistant in each of the departments of Humanity, Greek, Mathematics, and Natural Philosophy, and for two in the department of Chemistry ; and McFarlane's position was somewhat improved. His veneration for Thomson was such as few students or assistants have had for a master : his devotion resembled that of the old *famulus* rather than the much more measured respect paid by modern assistants to their chiefs.

After his retirement McFarlane lived on in Glasgow, and amused himself reading out-of-the-way Latin literature and with the calculation of eclipses! He finally returned to Alexandria, where he died in February 1897. "Old McFarlane" will be held in affectionate remembrance so long as students of the Natural Philosophy Class in the 'fifties and 'sixties and 'seventies, now, alas! a fast vanishing band, survive.

Soon after taking his degree of B.A. at Cambridge in 1845, Thomson had been elected a Fellow of St. Peter's College. In 1852 he vacated his Fellowship on his marriage to Miss Margaret Crum, daughter of Mr. Walter Crum of Thornliebank, near Glasgow, but was re-elected in 1871, and remained thereafter a Fellow of Peterhouse throughout his life.

CHAPTER VII

THE meeting of Thomson and Joule at Oxford in 1847 was fraught with important results to the theory of heat. Thomson had previously become acquainted with Carnot's essay, most probably through Clapeyron's account of it in the *Journal de l'École Polytechnique*, 1834, and had adopted Carnot's view that when work was done by a heat engine heat was merely let down from a body at one temperature to a body at a lower temperature. Joule apparently knew nothing of Carnot's theory, and had therefore come to the consideration of the subject without any preconceived opinions. He had thus been led to form a clear notion of heat as something which could be transformed into work, and *vice versa*. This was the root idea of his attempt to find the dynamical equivalent of heat. It was obvious that a heat engine took heat from a source and gave heat to a refrigerator, and Joule naturally concluded that the appearance of the work done by the engine must be accompanied by the disappearance of a quantity of heat of which the work done was the equivalent. He carried this idea consistently through all his work upon energy-changes, not merely in heat engines but in what might be called electric engines.

For he pointed out that the heat produced in the circuit of a voltaic battery was the equivalent of the energy-changes within the battery, and that, moreover, when an electromagnetic engine was driven by the current, or when electro-chemical decomposition was effected in a voltameter in the circuit, the heat evolved in the circuit for a given expenditure of the materials of the battery was less than it would otherwise have been, by the equivalent of the work done by the engine, or of the chemical changes effected in the voltameter. Thus Joule was in possession at an earlier date than Thomson of the fundamental notion upon which the true dynamical theory of heat engines is founded. Thomson, on the other hand, as soon as he had received this idea, was able to add to it the conception, derived from Carnot, of a reversible engine as the engine of greatest efficiency, and to deduce in a highly original manner all the consequences of these doctrines which go to make up the ordinary thermodynamics even of the present time. Though Clausius was the first, as we shall see, to deduce various important theorems, yet Thomson's discussion of the question had a quality peculiarly its own. It was marked by that freedom from unstated assumptions, from extraneous considerations, from vagueness of statement and of thought, which characterises all his applications of mathematics to physics. The physical ideas are always set forth clearly and in such a manner that their quantitative representation is immediate : we shall have an example of this in the doctrine of absolute temperature. In most of the thermodynamical discussions which take the great memoir of Clausius as their starting point, temperature is supposed to be given by a hypothetical something which is called a perfect gas, and it is very difficult, if not impossible, to gather a precise notion of the properties of such a gas and of the temperature scale thereon founded. Thomson's scale enables a perfect gas to be defined, and the deviations of the properties of ordinary gases from those of such a gas to be observed and measured.

The idea, then, which Joule had communicated to Section A, when Thomson interposed to call attention to its importance, was that work spent in overcoming friction had its equivalent in the heat produced, that, in fact, the amount of heat generated in such a case was proportional to the work spent, quite irrespective of the materials used in the process, provided no change of the internal energy of any of them took place so as to affect the resulting quantity of heat. This forced upon physicists the view pointed to by the doctrine of the immateriality of heat, established by the experiments of Rumford and Davy, that heat itself was a form of energy; and thus the principle of conservation of energy was freed from its one defect, its apparent failure when work was done against friction.

Rumford had noted the very great evolution of heat when gun-metal was rubbed by a blunt borer, and had come to the reasonable conclusion that what was evolved in apparently unlimited quantity by the abrasion or cutting down of a negligible quantity of materials could not be a material substance. He had also made a rough estimate of the relation between the work spent in driving the borer by horse-power and the heat generated. Joule's method of determining the work-equivalent of heat was a refinement of Rumford's, but differed in the all-important respect that accurate means were employed for measuring the expenditure of work and the gain of heat. He stirred a liquid, such as water or mercury, in a kind of churn driven by a falling weight. The range of descent of the weight enabled the work consumed to be exactly estimated, and a sensitive thermometer in the liquid measured the rise of temperature; thus the heat produced was accurately determined. The rise of temperature was very slight, and the change of state of the liquid, and therefore any possible change in its internal energy, was infinitesimal. The experiments were carried out with great care, and included very exact measurements of the various corrections—for example, the amount of work spent at pulleys and pivots without affecting the liquid, and the loss of heat by radiation. The experiments proved that the work spent on the liquid and the heat produced were in direct proportion to one another. He found, finally, in 1850, that 772 foot-pounds of work at Manchester generated one British thermal unit, that is, as much heat as sufficed to raise a pound of water from 60° F. to 61° F. An approximation to this conclusion was contained in the paper which he communicated to the British Association at Oxford in 1847.

The results of a later determination made with an improved apparatus, and completed in 1878, gave a very slightly higher result. When corrected to the corresponding Fahrenheit degree on the air thermometer it must be increased by somewhat less than one per cent. The exact relation has been the subject during the last twenty years of much refined experimental work, but without any serious alteration of the number indicated above.

It is probable that in consequence of the conference which he had with Joule at Oxford Thomson had his thoughts turned for some time almost exclusively to the dynamical theory of heat engines. He worked at the subject almost continuously for a long time, sending paper after paper to the Edinburgh Royal Society. As we have seen, he had given Joule a description of Carnot's essay on the Motive Power of Heat and the conclusions, or some of them, therein contained. Joule's result, and the thermodynamic law which it established, gave the key to the correction of Carnot's theory necessary to bring it into line with a complete doctrine of energy, which should take account of work done against frictional resistances.

Mayer of Heilbronn had endeavoured to determine the dynamical equivalent of heat in 1842, by calculating from the knowledge available at the time of the two specific heats of air—the specific heat at constant pressure and the specific heat at constant volume—the heat value of the work spent in compressing air from a given volume to a smaller one. The principle of this determination is easily understood, but it involves an assumption that is not always clearly perceived. Let the air be imagined confined in a cylinder closed by a frictionless piston, which is kept from moving out under the air pressure by force applied from without. Let heat be given to the air so as to raise its temperature, while the piston moves out so as to keep the pressure constant. If the pressure be p and the increase of volume be dv, the work done against the external force is pdv. Let the rise of temperature be one degree of the Centigrade scale, and the mass of air be one gramme, the heat given to the gas

is the specific heat C_p of the gas at constant pressure,
for there is only slight variation of specific heat with
temperature. But if the piston had been fixed the heat
required for the same rise of temperature would have
been C_v, the specific heat at constant volume. Now
Mayer assumed that the excess of the specific heat C_p
above C_v was the thermal equivalent of the work pdv
done in the former case. Thus he obtained the equation $J(C_p - C_v) = pdv$, where J denotes the dynamical
equivalent of heat and C_p, C_v are taken in thermal
units. But if a be the coefficient of expansion of the air
under constant pressure (that is $1/273$), and v_0 be the
volume of the air at $0°$ C., we have $dv = av_0$, so that
$J(C_p - C_v) = apv_0$. Now if p be one atmosphere, say
$1·014 \times 10^6$ dynes per square centimetre, and the
temperature be the freezing point of water, the volume
of a gramme of air is $1/·001293$ in cubic centimetres.
Hence

$$J(C_p - C_v) = \frac{1·014 \times 10^6}{273 \times ·001293}$$

from which, if $C_p - C_v$ is known, the value of J can
be found.

In Mayer's time the difference of the specific heats
of air was imperfectly known, and so J could not be
found with anything like accuracy. From Regnault's
experiments on the specific heat at constant pressure, and
from the known ratio of the specific heats as deduced
from the velocity of sound combined with Regnault's
result, the value of $C_p - C_v$ may be taken as ·0686.
Thus J works out to $42·2 \times 10^6$, in ergs per calorie,
which is not far from the true value. Mayer obtained
a result equivalent to $36·5 \times 10^6$ ergs per calorie.

The assumption on which this calculation is founded is that there is no alteration of the internal energy of the gas in consequence of expansion. If the air when raised in temperature, and at the same time increased in volume, contained less internal energy than when simply heated without alteration of volume, the energy evolved would be available to aid the performance of the work done against external forces, and less heat would be required, or, in the contrary case, more heat would be required, than would be necessary if the internal energy remained unaltered. Thus putting dW for pdv, the work done, e for the internal energy before expansion, and dH for the heat given to the gas, we have obviously the equation

$$JdH = de + dW$$

where de is the change of internal energy due to the alteration of volume, together with the alteration of temperature. If now the temperature be altered without expansion, no external work is done and dW for that case is zero. Let ∂e and ∂H be the energy change and the heat supplied, then in this case

$$J\partial H = \partial e + \text{o}$$
Thus $$J(dH - \partial H) = de - \partial e + dW$$

and the assumption is that $de = \partial e$, so that $dW = J(dH - \partial H)$; that is, $dW = J(C_p - C_v)$, when the rise of temperature is $1°$ C. and the mass of air is one gramme. This assumption requires justification, and by an experiment of Joule's, which was repeated in a more sensitive form devised by Thomson, it was shown to be a very close approximation to the truth.   Joule's experiment is well known : the explanation given above may serve to make clear the nature of the research undertaken later by Thomson and Joule conjointly.

The inverse process, the conversion of heat into work, required investigation, and it is this that constitutes the science of thermodynamics.   It was the subject of the celebrated *Réflexions sur la Puissance Motrice du Feu, et sur les Machines Propres à Développer cette Puissance*, published in 1824 by Sadi Carnot, an uncle of the late President of the French Republic.   Only a few copies of this essay were issued, and its text was known to very few persons twenty-four years later, when it was reprinted by the Academy of Sciences.   Its methods and conclusions were set forth by Thomson in 1849 in a memoir which he entitled, " An Account of Carnot's Theory of the Motive Power of Heat."   Numerical results deduced from Regnault's experiments on steam were included ; and the memoir as a whole led naturally in Thomson's hands to a corrected theory of heat engines, which he published in 1852.   Carnot's view of the working of a heat engine was founded on the analogy of the performance of work by a stream of water descending from a higher level to a lower. The same quantity of water flows away in a given time from a water wheel in the tail-race as is received in that time by the wheel from the supply stream. Now a heat engine receives heat from a supplying body, or source, at one temperature and parts with heat to another body (for example, the condenser of a steam engine) at a lower temperature.   This body is usually called the refrigerator.   According to Carnot these temperatures corresponded to the two levels in the case of the water wheel; the heat was what flowed through the engine. Thus in his theory as much heat was given up by a heat engine to the body at the lower temperature as was received by it from the source. The heat was simply transferred from the body at the higher temperature to the body at the lower; and this transference was supposed to be the source of the work.[1]

The first law of thermodynamics based on Joule's proportionality of heat produced to work expended, and the converse assumed and verified *a posteriori*, showed that this view is erroneous, and that the heat delivered to the refrigerator must be less in amount than that received from the source, by exactly the amount which is converted into work, together with the heat which, in an imperfect engine, is lost by conduction, etc., from the cylinder or other working chamber. This change was made by Thomson in his second paper : but he found the ideas of Carnot of direct and fruitful application in the new theory. These were the cycle of operations and the ideal reversible engine.

In the Carnot cycle the working substance—which might be a gas or a vapour, or a liquid, or a vapour and its liquid in contact : it did not matter what for the result—was supposed to be put through a succession of changes in which the final state coincided with the initial. Thus the substance having been brought

---

[1] Before his death (in 1832) Carnot had obtained a clear perception of the true state of the case, and of the complete doctrine of the conservatism of energy. [See extracts from Carnot's unpublished writings appended, with a biography, to the reprinted Memoir, by his younger brother, Hippolyte Carnot.]

back to the same physical condition as it had when the cycle began, has the same internal energy as it had at the beginning, and in the reckoning of the work done by or against external forces, nothing requires to be set to the account of the working substance. This is the first great advantage of the method of reasoning which Carnot introduced.

The ideal engine was a very simple affair : but the notion of reversibility is difficult to express in a form sufficiently definite and precise. Carnot does not attempt this ; he merely contents himself with describing certain cycles of operations which obviously can be carried through in the reverse order. Nor does Thomson go further in his "Account of Carnot's Theory," though he states the criterion of a perfect engine in the words, "A perfect thermodynamic engine is such that, whatever amount of mechanical effect it can derive from a certain thermal agency, if an equal amount be spent in working it backwards, an equal reverse thermal effect will be produced." This proposition was proved by Carnot : and the following formal statement in the essay is made : "La puissance motrice de la chaleur est independante des agents mis en œuvre pour la réaliser : sa quantité est fixée uniquement par les temperatures des corps entre lesquels se fait, en dernier résultat, le transport du calorique." The result involved in each, that the work done in a cycle by an ideal engine depends on the temperatures between which it works and not at all on the working substance, is, as we shall see, of the greatest importance. The proof of the proposition, by supposing a more efficient engine than the ideal one to exist, and to be coupled with the latter, so that the more efficient would perform the cycle forwards and the ideal engine the same cycle backwards, is well known. In Carnot's view the former would do more work by letting down a given quantity of heat from the higher to the lower temperature than was spent on the latter in transferring the same quantity of heat from the lower to the higher temperature, so that no heat would be taken from or given to source or refrigerator, while there would be a gain of work on the whole. This would be equivalent to admitting that useful work could be continually performed without any resulting thermal or other change in the agents performing the work. Even at that time this could not be admitted as possible, and hence the supposition that a more efficient engine than the reversible one could exist was untenable.

Carnot showed that the work done by an ideal engine, in transferring heat from one temperature to another, was to be found by means of a certain function of the temperature, hence called "Carnot's function." The corresponding function in the true dynamical theory is always called Carnot's. A certain assignment of value to it gave, as we shall see, Thomson's famous absolute thermodynamic scale of temperature.

In the light of the facts and theories which now exist, and are almost the commonplaces of physical text books, it is very interesting to review the ideas and difficulties which occurred to the founders of the science of heat sixty years ago. For example, Thomson asks, in his "Account of Carnot's Theory," what becomes of the mechanical effect which might be produced by heat which is transferred from one body to another by conduction. The heat leaves one body

and enters another and no mechanical effect results :
if it passed from one to the other through a heat
engine, mechanical effect would be produced : what is
produced in place of the mechanical effect which is
lost ? This he calls a very " perplexing question," and
hopes that it will, before long, be cleared up. He
states, further, that the difficulty would be entirely
avoided by abandoning Carnot's principle that mechanical effect is obtained by " the transference of heat from
one body to another at a lower temperate." Joule urges
precisely this solution of the difficulty in his paper,
" On the Changes of Temperature produced by the
Rarefaction and Condensation of Air" (*Phil. Mag.*, May
1845). Thomson notes this, but adds, " If we do so,
however, we meet with innumerable other difficulties—
insuperable without further experimental investigation,
and an entire reconstruction of the theory of heat from
its foundation. It is in reality to experiment that we
must look, either for a verification of Carnot's axiom,
and an explanation of the difficulty we have been considering, or for an entirely new basis of the Theory of
Heat."

The experiments here asked for had already, as was
soon after perceived by Thomson, been made by Joule,
not merely in his determinations of the dynamical
equivalent of heat, but in his exceedingly important
investigation of the energy changes in the circuit of a
voltaic cell, or of a magneto-electric machine. Moreover, the answer to this " very perplexing question "
was afterwards to be given by Thomson himself in his
paper, " On a Universal Tendency in Nature to the
Dissipation of Mechanical Energy," published in the
Edinburgh *Proceedings* in 1852.

Again, we find, a page or two earlier in the "Account of Carnot's Theory," the question asked with respect to the heat evolved in the circuit of a magneto-electric machine, "Is the heat which is evolved in one part of the closed conductor merely transferred from those parts which are subject to the inducing influence?" and the statement made that Joule had examined this question, and decided that it must be answered in the negative. But Thomson goes on to say, "Before we can finally conclude that heat is absolutely generated in such operations, it would be necessary to prove that the inducing magnet does not become lower in temperature and thus compensate for the heat evolved in the conductor."

Here, apparently, the idea of work done in moving the magnet, or the conductor in the magnetic field, is not present to Thomson's mind ; for if it had been, the idea that the work thus spent might have its equivalent, in part, at least, in heat generated in the circuit, would no doubt have occurred to him and been stated. This idea had been used just a year before by Helmholtz, in his essay "Die Erhaltung der Kraft," to account for the heat produced in the circuit by the induced current, that is, to answer the first question put above in the sense in which Joule answered it. The subject, however, was fully worked out by Thomson in a paper published in the *Philosophical Magazine* for December 1851, to which we shall refer later.

Tables of the work performed by various steam engines working between different stated temperatures were given at the close of the "Account," and compared with the theoretical "duty" as calculated for

Carnot's ideal perfect engine. Of course the theoretical
duty was calculated from the temperatures of the boiler
and condenser ; the much greater fall of temperature
from the furnace to the boiler was neglected as
inevitable, so that the loss involved in that fall is not
taken account of.   Carnot's   theory gave for the
theoretical duty of one heat unit (equivalent to 1390
foot-pounds of work) 440 foot-pounds for boiler at
140° C. and condenser at 30° C. ; and the best performance recorded was 253 foot-pounds, giving a percentage
of 57·5 per cent. The worst was that of common engines
consuming 12lb. of coal per horse-power per hour, and
gave 38·1 foot-pounds, or a percentage of 8·6 per cent.
These percentages become on the dynamical theory
68 and 10·3, since the true theoretical duty for the
heat unit is only 371 foot-pounds.

It is worthy of notice that the indicator-diagram
method of graphically representing the changes in a
cycle of operations is adopted in Thomson's " Account,"
but does not occur in Carnot's essay. The cycles
consist of two isothermal changes and two adiabatic
changes ; that is, two changes at the temperatures of
the source and refrigerator respectively, and two
changes—from the higher to the lower temperature,
and from the lower to the higher. These changes are
made subject to the condition in each case that the
substance neither gains nor loses energy in the form of
heat, but is cooled in the one case by expansion and
heated in the other by compression. The indicator
diagram was due not to Thomson but to Clapeyron
(see p. 99 above), who used it to illustrate an account
of Carnot's theory.

There appeared in the issue of the Edinburgh

Philosophical Transactions for January 2, 1849, along with the " Account of Carnot's Theory," a paper by James Thomson, entitled, "Theoretical Considerations on the Effect of Pressure in Lowering the Freezing Point of Water." The author predicted that, unless the principle of conservation of energy was at fault, the effect of increase of pressure on water in the act of freezing would be to lower the freezing point ; and he calculated from Carnot's theory the amount of lowering which would be produced by a given increment of pressure. The prediction thus made was tested by experiments carried out in the Physical Laboratory by Thomson, and the results obtained completely confirmed the conclusions arrived at by theory. This prediction and its verification have been justly regarded as of great importance in the history of the dynamical theory of heat ; and they afford an excellent example of the predictive character of a true scientific theory. The theory of the matter will be referred to in the next chapter.

CHAPTER VIII

THE first statement of the true dynamical theory of heat, based on the fundamental idea that the work done in a Carnot cycle is to be accounted for by an excess of the heat received from the source over the heat delivered to the refrigerator, was given by Clausius in a paper which appeared in *Poggendorff's Annalen* in March and April 1850, and in the *Philosophical Magazine* for July 1850, under a title which is a German translation of that of Carnot's essay. In that paper the First Law of Thermodynamics is explicitly stated as follows : "In all cases in which work is produced by the agency of heat, a quantity of heat proportional to the amount of work produced is expended, and, inversely, by the expenditure of that amount of work exactly the same amount of heat is generated." Modern thermodynamics is based on this principle and on the so-called Second Law of Thermodynamics ; which is, however, variously stated by different authors. According to Clausius, who used in his paper an argument like that of Carnot based on the transference of heat from the source to the refrigerator, the foundation of the second law was the fact that heat tends to pass from hotter to colder bodies. In 1854 (*Pogg. Ann.*, Dec. 1854) he stated his fundamental principle explicitly in the form : "Heat can never

114

pass from a colder to a hotter body, unless some other change, connected therewith, take place at the same time," and gives in a note the shorter statement, which he regards as equivalent : " Heat cannot of itself pass from a colder to a hotter body."

We shall not here discuss the manner in which Clausius applied this principle : but he arrived at and described in his paper many important results, of which he must therefore be regarded as the primary discoverer. His theory as originally set forth was lacking in clearness and simplicity, and was much improved by additions made to it on its re-publication, in 1864, with other memoirs on the Theory of Heat.

In the *Transactions R.S.E.*, for March 1851, Thomson published his great paper, "On the Dynamical Theory of Heat." The object of the paper was stated to be threefold : (1) To show what modifications of Carnot's conclusions are required, when the dynamical theory is adopted : (2) To indicate the significance in this theory of the numerical results deduced from Regnault's observations on steam : (3) To point out certain remarkable relations connecting the physical properties of all substances established by reasoning analogous to that of Carnot, but founded on the dynamical theory.

This paper, though subsequent to that of Clausius, is very different in character. Many of the results are identical with those previously obtained by Clausius, but they are reached by a process which is preceded by a clear statement of fundamental principles. These principles have since been the subject of discussion, and are not free from difficulty even now ; but a great step in advance was made by their careful formulation in

Thomson's paper, as a preliminary to the erection of the theory and the deduction of its consequences. Two propositions are stated which may be taken as the First and Second Laws of Thermodynamics. One is equivalent to the First Law as stated in p. 116, the other enunciates the principle of Reversibility as a criterion of "perfection" of a heat engine. We quote these propositions.

"Prop. I. (Joule).—When equal quantities of mechanical effect are produced by any means whatever from purely thermal sources, or lost in purely thermal effects, equal quantities of heat are put out of existence or are generated."

"Prop. II (Carnot and Clausius).—If an engine be such that when worked backwards, the physical and mechanical agencies in every part of its motions are all reversed, it produces as much mechanical effect as can be produced by any thermodynamic engine, with the same temperatures of source and refrigerator, from a given quantity of heat."

Prop. I was proved by assuming that heat is a form of energy and considering always the work effected by causing a working substance to pass through a closed cycle of changes, so that there was no change of internal energy to be reckoned with.

Prop. II was proved by the following "axiom": "It is impossible, by means of inanimate material agency, to derive mechanical effect from any portion of matter by cooling it below the temperature of the coldest of the surrounding objects." This is rather a postulate than an axiom; for it can hardly be contended that it commands assent as soon as it is stated, even from a mind which is conversant with thermal phenomena.

It sets forth clearly, however, and with sufficient guardedness of statement, a principle which, when the process by which work is done is always a cyclical one, is not found contradicted by experience, and one, moreover, which can be at once explicitly applied to demonstrate that no engine can be more efficient than a reversible one, and that therefore the efficiency of a reversible engine is independent of the nature of the working substance.

It has been suggested by Clerk Maxwell that this "axiom" is contradicted by the behaviour of a gas. According to the kinetic theory of gases an elevation of temperature consists in an increase of the kinetic energy of the translatory motion of the gaseous particles ; and no doubt there actually is, from time to time, a passage of some more quickly moving particles from a portion of a gas in which the average kinetic energy is low, to a region in which the average kinetic energy is high, and thus a transference of heat from a region of low temperature to one of higher temperature.   Maxwell imagined a space filled with gas to be divided into two compartments A and B by a partition in which were small massless trapdoors, to open and shut which required no expenditure of energy.   At each of these doors was stationed a "sorting demon," whose duty it was to allow every particle having a velocity greater than the average to pass through from A to B, and to stop all those of smaller velocity than the average.   Similarly, the demons were to prevent all quickly moving particles from going across from B to A, and to pass all slowly moving particles. In this way, without the expenditure of work, all the quickly moving particles could be assembled in one compartment, and all the slowly moving particles in the other ; and thus a difference of temperatures between the two compartments could be brought about, or a previously existing one increased by transference of heat from a colder to a hotter mass of gas.

Contrary to a not uncommon belief, this process does not invalidate Thomson's axiom as he intended it to be understood. For the gas referred to here is what he would have regarded as the working substance of the engine, by the cycles of which all the mechanical effect was derived ; and it is not, at the end of the process, in the state as regards average kinetic energy of the particles in which it was at first. That this was his answer to the implied criticism of his axiom contained in Maxwell's illustration, those who have heard him refer to the matter in his lectures are well aware. But of course it is to be understood that the substance returns to the same state only in a statistical sense.

Thomson's demonstration that a reversible engine is the most efficient is well known, and need not here be repeated in detail. The reversible engine may be worked backwards, and the working substance will take in heat where in the direct action it gave it out, and *vice versa :* the substance will do work against external forces where in the direct action it had work done upon it, and *vice versa :* in short, all the physical and mechanical changes will be of the same amount, but merely reversed, at every stage of the backward process. Thus if an engine A be more efficient than a reversible one B, it will convert a larger percentage of an amount of heat H taken in at the source into work than would the reversible one working between the same temperatures. Thus if h be the heat given to the refrigerator by A, and h' that given by B when both work directly and take in H; h must be less than h'. Then couple the engines together so that B works backwards while A works directly. A will take in H and deliver h, and do work equivalent to $H - h$. B will take h' from the refrigerator and deliver H to the source, and have work equivalent to $H - h'$ spent upon it. There will be no heat on the whole given to or taken from the source; but heat $h' - h$ will be taken from the refrigerator, and work equivalent to this will be done. Thus *by a cyclical process*, which leaves the working substance as it was, work is done at the expense of heat taken from the refrigerator, which Thomson's postulate affirms to be impossible. Therefore the assumption that an engine more efficient than the reversible engine exists must be abandoned; and we have the conclusion that all reversible engines are equally efficient.

Thomson acknowledged in his paper the priority of Clausius in his proof of this proposition, but stated that this demonstration had occurred to him before he was aware that Clausius had dealt with the matter. He now cited, as examples of the First Law of Thermodynamics, the results of Joule's experiments regarding the heat produced in the circuits of magneto-electric machines, and the fact that when an electric current produced by a thermal agency or by a battery drives a motor, the heat evolved in the circuit by the passage of the current is lessened by the equivalent of the work done on the motor.

In the Carnot cycle, the first operation is an isothermal expansion (AB in Fig. 12), in which the substance increases in volume by dv, and takes in from

the source heat of amount Mdv. The second
operation is an adiabatic expansion, BC, in which
the volume is further increased and the temperature
sinks by dt to the temperature of the refrigerator.
The third operation is an isothermal compression,
CD, until the volume and pressure are such that
an adiabatic compression DA will just bring the
substance back to the original state. If $\partial p \,/\, \partial t$ be the

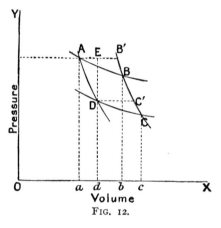

FIG. 12.

rate of increase of pressure with temperature when
the volume is constant, the step of pressure from one
isothermal to the other is $\partial p/\,\partial t \,.\, dt$; and thus the area
of the closed cycle in the diagram which measures the
external work done in the succession of changes is
$\partial p \,/\, \partial t \,.\, dtdv$. Now, by the second law, the work done
must be a certain fraction of the work-equivalent of
the heat, Mdv, taken in from the source. This
fraction is independent of the nature of the working
substance, but varies with the temperature, and is

therefore a function of the temperature. Its ratio to the difference of temperature dt between source and refrigerator was called " Carnot's function," and the determination of this function by experiment was at first perhaps the most important problem of thermodynamics. Denoting it by μ, we have the equation

$$\frac{\partial p}{\partial t} = \mu M \quad . \quad . \quad . \quad . \quad (A)$$

which may be taken as expressing in mathematical language the second law of thermodynamics. M is here so chosen that Mdv is the heat expressed in units of work, so that μ does not involve Joule's equivalent of heat. This equation was given by Carnot: it is here obtained by the dynamical theory which regards the work done as accounted for by disappearance, not transference merely, of heat.

The work done in the cycle becomes now $\mu Mdtdv$, or if H denote Mdv, it is μHdt. The fraction of the heat utilised is thus μdt. This is called the *efficiency* of the engine for the cycle.

From the first law Thomson obtained another fundamental equation. For every substance there is a relation connecting the pressure p (or more generally the stress of some type), the volume v (or the configuration according to the specified stress), and the temperature. We may therefore take arbitrary changes of any two of these quantities: the relation referred to will give the corresponding change of the third. Thomson chose v and t as the quantities to be varied, and supposed them to sustain arbitrary small changes dv and dt in consequence of the passage of heat to the substance from without. The amount of heat taken in is $Mdv + Ndt$, where Mdv and Ndt are heats required for the changes taken separately. But the substance expanding through dv does external work pdv. Thus the net amount of energy given to the substance from without is $Mdv + Ndt - pdv$ or $(M - p)dv + Ndt$; and if the substance is made to pass through a cycle of changes so that it returns to the physical state from which it started, the whole energy received in the cycle must be zero. From this it follows that the rate of variation of $M - p$ when the temperature but not the volume varies, is equal to the rate of variation of N when the volume but not the temperature varies. To see that this relation holds, the reader unacquainted with the properties of perfect differentials may proceed thus. Let the substance be subjected to the infinitesimal closed cycle of changes defined by (1) a variation consisting of the simultaneous changes dv, dt of volume and temperature, (2) a variation $-dv$ of volume only, (3) a variation $-dt$ of temperature only. $M - p$ and N vary so as to have definite values for the beginning and end of each step, and the proper mean values can be written down for each step at once, and therefore the value of $(M - p)\, dv + Ndt$ obtained. Adding together these values for the three steps we get the integral for the cycle. The condition that this should vanish is at once seen to be the relation stated above.

This result combined with the equation A derived from the second law, gives an important expression for Carnot's function.

We shall not pursue this discussion further : so much is given to make clear how certain results as to the physical properties of substances were obtained, and to explain Thomson's scale of absolute thermodynamic temperature, which is by far the most important discovery within the range of theoretical thermodynamics.

There are several scales of temperature : in point of fact the scale of a mercury-in-glass thermometer is defined by the process of graduation, and therefore there are as many such scales as there are thermometers, since no two specimens of glass expand in precisely the same way. Equal differences of temperature do not correspond to equal increments of volume of the mercury : for the glass envelope expands also and in its own way. On the scale of a constant pressure gas thermometer changes of temperature are measured by variations of volume of the gas, while the pressure is maintained constant ; on a constant volume gas thermometer changes of temperature are measured by alterations of pressure while the volume of the gas is kept constant. Each scale has its own independent definition, thus if the pressure of the gas be kept constant, and the volume at temperature $0°$ C. be v_0, and that at any other temperature be v_1, we define the numerical value t, this latter temperature, by the equation $v = v_0 (1 + Et)$, where E is $1 / 100$ of the increase of volume sustained by the gas in being raised from $0°$ C. to $100°$ C. These are the temperatures of reference on an ordinary centigrade thermometer, that is, the temperature of melting ice and of saturated steam under standard atmospheric pressure, respectively. Thus t has the value $(v / v_0 - 1) / E$, and is the temperature (on the constant pressure scale of the gas thermometer) corresponding to the volume v. Equal differences of temperature are such as correspond to equal increments of the volume at $0°$ C.

Similarly, on the constant volume scale we obtain a definition of temperature from the pressure p, by the equation $t = (p/p_0 - 1)/E'$, where p_0 is the pressure at $0°$ C., and E' is $1/100$ of the change of pressure produced by raising the temperature from $0°$ C. to $100°$ C.

For air E is approximately $1/273$, and thus $t = 273 (v - v_0)/v_0$. If we take the case of $v = 0$, we get $t = -273$. Now, although this temperature may be inaccessible, we may take it as zero, and the temperature denoted by t is, when reckoned from this zero, $273 + t$. This zero is called the absolute zero on the constant pressure air thermometer. The value of E' is very nearly the same as that of E; and we get in a similar manner an absolute zero for the constant volume scale. If the gas obeyed Boyle's law exactly at all temperatures, E would not differ from E'.

It was suggested to Thomson by Joule, in a letter dated December 9, 1848, that the value of μ might be given by the equation $\mu = JE/(1 + Et)$. Here we take heat in dynamical units, and therefore the factor J is not required. With these units Joule's suggestion is that $\mu = E/(1 + Et)$, or with $E = 1/273$ $\mu = 1/(273 + t)$, that is, $\mu = 1/T$ where T is the temperature reckoned in centigrade degrees from the absolute zero of the constant pressure air thermometer.

The possibility of adopting this value of μ was shown by Thomson to depend on whether or not the heat absorbed by a given mass of gas in expanding without alteration of temperature is the equivalent of the work done by the expanding gas against external pressure.

The heat H absorbed by the air in expanding from volume V to another volume V' at constant temperature is the integral of $M\,dv$ taken from the former volume to the latter. But by the value of M given on p. 121, if W be the integral of $p\,dv$, that is the work done by the air in the expansion, $\partial W / \partial t = \mu H$. The equation fulfilled by the gas at constant pressure (the defining equation for t), $v = v_0(1 + Et)$, gives for the integral of $p\,dv$, that is W, the equation $W = pv_0(1 + Et) \log(V'/V)$, so that $\partial W / \partial t = EW / (1 + Et)$. Thus $\mu H = EW / (1 + Et)$.

Hence it follows that if $\mu = E / (1 + Et)$, the value of H will be simply W. Thus Joule's suggested value of μ is only admissible if the work done by the gas in expanding from a given volume to any other is the equivalent of the heat absorbed ; or, which is the same thing, if the external work done in compressing the gas from one volume to another is the equivalent of the heat developed.

This result naturally suggests the formation of a new scale of thermometry by the adoption of the defining relation $T = 1/\mu$, where T denotes temperature. A scale of temperature thus defined is proposed in the paper by Joule and Thomson, " On the Thermal Effects of Fluids in Motion," Part II, which was published in the *Philosophical Transactions* for June 1854, and is what is now universally known as Thomson's scale of absolute thermodynamic temperature. It can, of course, be made to give 100 as the numerical value of the temperature difference between 0° C. and 100° C. by properly fixing the unit of T. This scale was the natural successor, in the dynamical theory, of one which Thomson had suggested in 1848, and which was founded, according to Carnot's idea, on the condition that a unit of heat should do the same amount of work in descending through each degree. This, as he pointed out, might justly be called an *absolute* scale, since it would be independent of the physical properties of any substance. In the same sense the scale defined by $T = 1 / \mu$ is truly an absolute scale.

The new scale gives a simple expression for the efficiency of a perfect engine working between two physically given temperatures, and assigns the numerical values of these temperatures; for the heat H taken in from the source in the isothermal expansion which forms the first operation of the cycle (p. 120) is Mdv, and, as we have seen, the work done in the cycle is $\partial p / \partial t . dtdv$, or μHdt. If we adopt the expression $1 / T$ for μ, we may put dT for dt; and we obtain for the work done the expression HdT / T. The work done is thus the fraction dT / T of the heat taken in, and this is what is properly called the efficiency of the engine for the cycle.

If we suppose the difference of temperatures between source and refrigerator to be finite, $T - T'$, say, then since T is the temperature of the source, we have for the efficiency $(T - T') / T$. If the heat taken in be H, the heat rejected is HT' / T, so that the heat received by the engine is to the heat rejected by it in the ratio of T' to T. Thus, as was done by Thomson, we may define the temperatures of the source and refrigerator as proportional to the heat taken in from the source and the heat rejected to the refrigerator by a perfect engine, working between those temperatures. The scale may be made to have 100 degrees between the temperature of melting ice and the boiling point, as already explained. We shall return to the comparison of this scale with that of the air thermometer. At present we consider some of the thermodynamic relations of the properties of bodies arrived at by Thomson.

First we take the working substance of the engine as consisting of matter in two states or phases; for example, ice and water, or water and saturated steam. Let us apply equation (A) to this case. If v_1, v_2 be the volume of unit of mass in the first and second states respectively, the isothermal expansion of the first part of the cycle will take place in consequence of the conversion of a mass dm from the first state to the second. Thus dv, the change of volume, is $dm (v_2 - v_1)$. Also if L be the latent heat of the substance in the second state, *e.g.* the latent heat of water, $Mdv = Ldm$; so that $M (v_2 - v_1) = L$. If dp be the step of pressure corresponding to the step dT of temperature, equation (A) becomes

$$\frac{dT}{T} = dp \frac{v_2 - v_1}{L} \quad . \quad . \quad . \quad (B)$$

In the case of coexistence of the liquid and solid phases, this gives us the very remarkable result that a change of pressure dp will raise or lower the temperature of coexistence of the two phases, that is, the melting point of the solid, by the difference of temperature, dT, according as v_2 is greater or less than v_1. Thus a substance like water, which expands in freezing, so that $v_2 - v_1$ is negative, has its freezing point lowered by increase of pressure and raised by diminution of pressure. This is the result predicted by Professor James Thomson and verified experimentally by his brother (p. 113 above). On the other hand, a substance like paraffin wax, which contracts in solidifying, would have its melting point raised by increase of pressure and lowered by a diminution of pressure.

The same conclusions would be applicable when the phases are liquid and vapour of the same substance, if there were any case in which $v_2 - v_1$ is negative. As it is we see, what is well known to be the case, that the temperature of equilibrium of a liquid with its vapour is raised by increase of pressure.

Another important result of equation (B), as applied to the liquid and vapour phases of a substance, is the information which it gives as to the density of the saturated vapour. When the two phases coexist the pressure is a function of the temperature only. Hence if the relation of pressure to temperature is known, dp / dT can be calculated, or obtained graphically from a curve ; and the volume v_2 per unit mass of the vapour will be given in terms of dp / dT, the temperature T, and the volume v per unit mass of the liquid. The density of saturated steam at different temperatures is very difficult to measure experimentally with any approach of accuracy : but so far as experiment goes equation (B) is confirmed. The theory here given is fully confirmed by other results, and equation (B) is available for the calculation of v_2 for any substance for which the relation between p and T is known. It is thus that the density of saturated steam can best be found.

We can obtain another important result for the case of the working substance in two phases from equation (B). The relation is

$$\frac{\partial L}{\partial T} + c - h = \frac{L}{T} \quad . \quad . \quad . \quad . \quad (C)$$

where c and h are the specific heats of the substance in the two phases respectively, and L is the latent heat of the second phase at absolute temperature T.

We shall obtain the relation in another way, which will illustrate another mode of dealing with a cycle of operations which Thomson employed. Any small step of change of a substance may be regarded as made up of a step of volume, say, followed by a step of temperature, that is, by an isothermal step followed by an adiabatic step. In this way any cycle of operations whatever may be regarded as made up of a series of Carnot cycles. But without regarding any cycle of a more general kind than Carnot's as thus compounded, we can draw conclusions from it by the dynamical theory provided only it is reversible. Suppose a gramme, say, of the substance to be taken at a specified temperature T in the lower phase, and to be changed to the other phase at that temperature. The heat taken in will be L and the expansion will be $v_2 - v_1$. Next, keeping the substance in the second phase, and in equilibrium with the first phase (that is, for example, if the second phase is saturated vapour, the saturation is to continue in the further change), let the substance be lowered in temperature by dT. The heat given out by the substance will be $h dT$, where h is the specific heat of the substance in the second phase. Now at the new temperature $T - dT$ let the substance be wholly brought back to the second phase ; the heat given out will be $L - \partial L / \partial T . dT$. Finally, let the substance, now again all in the first phase, be brought to the original temperature : the heat taken in will be $c dt$, where c is the specific heat in the first phase. Thus the net excess of heat taken in over heat given out in the cycle is $(\partial L/\partial T + c - h)\, dT$. This must, in the indicator diagram for the changes specified, be the area of the cycle or $(v_2 - v_1)\, \partial p\, / \partial T$. dT. But by equation (B) $L/T\, (v_2 - v_1) = \partial p\, / \partial T$, and the area of the cycle is $(L/T)dT$. Equating the two expressions thus found for the area we get equation (C).

This relation was arrived at by Clausius in his paper referred to above, and the priority of publication is his : it is here given in the form which it takes when Thomson's scale of absolute temperature is used.

Regnault's experimental results for the heat required to raise unit mass of water from the temperature of melting ice to any higher temperature and evaporate it at that temperature enable the values of L/T and $\partial L\, / \partial T$ to be calculated, and therefore that of h to be found. It appears that h is negative for all the temperatures to which Regnault's experimental results can be held to apply. This, as was pointed out by Thomson, means that if a mass of saturated vapour is made to expand so as at the same time to fall in temperature, it must have heat given to it, otherwise it will be partly condensed into liquid ; and, on the other hand, if the vapour be compressed and made to rise in temperature while at the same time it is kept saturated, heat must be taken from it, otherwise the vapour will become superheated and so cease to be saturated.

It is convenient to notice here the article on *Heat* which Thomson wrote for the ninth edition of the *Encyclopædia Britannica*. In that article he gave a valuable discussion of ordinary thermometry, of thermometry by means of the pressures of saturated vapour of different substances—steam-pressure thermometers, he called them—of absolute thermodynamic thermometry, all enriched with new experimental and theoretical investigations, and appended to the whole a valuable synopsis, with additions of his own, of the Fourier mathematics of heat conduction.

First dealing with temperature as measured by the expansion of a liquid in a less expansible vessel, he showed how it is in reality numerically reckoned. This amounted to a discussion of the scale of an ordinary mercury-in-glass thermometer, a subject concerning which erroneous statements are not infrequently made in text-books. A sketch of Thomson's treatment of it is given here.

Considering this thermometer as a vessel consisting of a glass bulb and a long glass stem of fine and uniform bore, hermetically sealed and containing only mercury and mercury vapour, he explained the numerical relation between the temperature as shown by the instrument and the volumes of the mercury and vessel. The scale is really defined by the method of graduation adopted. Two points of reference are marked on the stem at which the top of the mercury stands when the vessel is immersed (1) in melting ice, (2) in saturated steam under standard atmospheric pressure. The stem is divided into parts of equal volume of bore between these two points and beyond each of them. For a centigrade thermometer the bore-space between the two points is divided into 100 equal parts, and the lower point of reference is marked 0 and the upper 100, and the other dividing marks are numbered in accordance with this along the stem. Each of these parts of the bore may be called a degree-space.

Now let the instrument contain in its bulb and stem, up to the mark 0, N degree-spaces, and let v be the volume of a degree-space at that temperature. The volume up to the mark o will be Nv, at that temperature ; and if the substance of the vessel be quite uniform in quality and free from stress, N will be the same for all temperatures. If v_0 be the volume of a degree-space at the temperature of melting ice the volume of the mercury at that temperature will be Nv_0. If G be the expansion of the glass when the volume of a degree-space is increased from v_0 to v by the rise of temperature, then $v = v_0 \, (1 + G)$. The volume of the mercury has been increased therefore to $(N + n) \, v_0 \, (1 + G)$ by the same rise of temperature, if the top of the column is thereby made to rise from the mark o so as to occupy n degree-spaces more than before. But if E be the expansion of the mercury between the temperature of melting ice and that which has now been attained, the volume of the mercury is also $Nv_0 \, (1 + E)$. Hence $N \, (1 + E) = (N + n) \, (1 + G)$. This gives $n = N(E - G)/(1 + G)$.

If we take, as is usual, n as measuring the temperature, and substitute for it the symbol t, we have, since $N = 100 \, (1 + G_{100}) / (E_{100} - G_{100})$,

$$ t = 100 \; \frac{1 + G_{100}}{1 + G} \; \frac{E - G}{E_{100} - G_{100}} \quad . \quad . \; (D) $$

In this reckoning the definition of any temperature, let us say $37°$ C., is the temperature of the vessel and its contents when the top of the mercury column stands at the mark 37 above o, on the scale defined by the graduation of the instrument ; but the numerical signification with relation to the volumes is given by equation (D). This shows that the numerical measure of any temperature involves both the expansion of the vessel and that of the glass vessel between the temperature of melting ice and the temperature in question. This result may be contrasted with the erroneous statement frequently made that equal increments of temperature correspond to equal increments of the volume of the thermometric substance. It also shows that different mercury-in-glass thermometers, however accurately made and graduated, need not agree when placed in a bath at any other temperature than 0° C. or 100° C. This fact, and the results of the comparison of thermometers made with different kinds of glass with the normal air thermometer, which was carried out by Regnault, were always insisted on by Thomson in his teaching when he dealt with the subject of heat. The scale of a mercury-in-glass thermometer is too often in text-books, and even in Acts of Parliament regarded as a perfectly definite thing, and the expansion of a gas is not infrequently defined by this indefinite scale, instead of being used as it ought to be, as the basis of definition of the scale of the gas thermometer. The whole treatment of the so-called gaseous laws is too often, from a logical point of view, a mass of confusion.

In his article on *Heat* Thomson gave two definitions of the scale of absolute temperature. One is that stated on p. 126 above, namely, that the temperature of the source and refrigerator are in the ratio of the heat taken in from the source to the heat given to the refrigerator, when the engine describes a Carnot cycle consisting of two isothermal and two adiabatic changes.

The other definition is better adapted for general use, as it applies to any cycle whatever which is reversible.

Let the working substance expand under constant pressure by an amount dv (AB' in Fig. 12), and let heat H be given to the substance at the same time. The external work done is pdv. Thomson called pdv / H the work ratio. Now let the temperature be raised by dT without giving heat to the substance or taking heat from it, and let the corresponding pressure rise be dp; and call dp / p the pressure ratio. The temperature ratio dT / T is equal to the product of the work ratio and the pressure ratio, that is,

$$\frac{dT}{T} = \frac{dv\,dp}{H}$$

This is clearly true; for $dv\,dp$ is the area of a cycle like $AB'C'D$, represented in Fig. 12, for which an amount of heat H is taken in, though not in this case strictly at one temperature. And clearly, since in Fig. 12 the change from B' to B is adiabatic, H is the heat which would have to be taken in for the isothermal change AB in the Carnot cycle $ABCD$, which has the same area as $AB'C'D$. Thus the efficiency of the cycle is $dv\,dp / H$, and this by the former definition is dT / T.

Or we may regard the matter thus :—The amount of heat H which corresponds to an infinitesimal expansion dv may be used in equation (A) whether the expansion is isothermal or not, if we take T as the average temperature of the expansion. Hence we have $dp / dT = H / (dv.T)$, that is, $dT / T = dp\,dv / H$. The theorem on p. 128 is obtained by what is virtually this process.

COMPARISON OF ABSOLUTE SCALE WITH SCALE OF AIR THERMOMETER

The comparison which Joule and Thomson carried out of the absolute thermodynamic scale with the scale of the constant pressure gas thermometer has already been referred to, and it has been shown that the two scales would exactly agree, that is, absolute temperature would be simply proportional to the volume of the gas in a gas thermometer kept at the temperature to be measured, if the internal energy of the gas were not altered by an alteration of volume without alteration of temperature, that is, if the $de - \partial e$ of p. 107 above were zero. Joule tested whether this was the case by immersing two vessels, connected by a tube which could be opened or closed by a stopcock, in the water of a calorimeter, ascertaining the temperature with a very sensitive thermometer, and then allowing air which had already been compressed into one of the vessels to flow into the other, which was initially empty. It was found that no alteration of temperature of the water of the calorimeter that could be observed was produced. But the volume of the air had been doubled by the process, and if any sensible alteration of internal energy had taken place it would have shown itself by an elevation or a lowering of the temperature of the water, according as the energy had been diminished or increased.

Thomson suggested that the gas to be examined should be forced through a pipe ending in a fine nozzle, or, preferably, through a plug of porous material placed in a pipe along which the gas was forced by a pump, and observations made of the temperature in the steady stream on both sides of the plug. The experiments were carried out with a plug of compressed cotton-wool held between two metal disks pierced with holes, in a tube of boxwood surrounded also by cotton-wool, and placed in a bath of water closely surrounding the supply pipe. This was of metal, and formed the end of a long spiral all immersed in the bath. Thus the temperature of the gas approaching the plug was kept at a uniform temperature determined by a delicate thermometer; another thermometer gave the temperature in the steady stream beyond the plug.

In the case of hydrogen the experiments showed a slight heating effect of passage through the plug; air, oxygen, nitrogen and carbonic acid were cooled by the passage.

The theory of the matter is set forth in the original papers, and in a very elegant manner in the article on *Heat*. The result of the analysis shows that if ∂w be the positive or negative work-value of the heat which will convert one gramme of the gas after passage to its original temperature; and T be absolute temperature, and v volume of a gramme of the gas at pressure p, and the difference of pressure on the two sides of the plug be dp, the equation which holds is

$$\frac{1}{T} \frac{\partial T}{\partial v} = \frac{1}{v + \dfrac{\partial w}{dp}} \quad . \quad . \quad . \quad (\text{E})[1]$$

[1] This equation for the porous plug experiment may be established in the following manner, which forms a good example of Thomson's second definition of absolute temperature. Take pressure and volume of the gas on the supply side of the plug as $p + dp$ and v, and on the delivery side as p and $v + dv$, so that dp and dv are positive. The net work done in forcing the gas through the plug $= (p + dp) v - p (v + dv) = -p\,dv + v\,dp$. Let a heating effect result

If there is neither heating nor cooling $\partial w = 0$, and we obtain by integration $T = Cv$, where C is a constant.

It was found by Joule and Thomson that ∂w was proportional to dp for values of dp up to five or six atmospheres. At different temperatures, however, in the case of hydrogen the heating effect was found to diminish with rise of temperature, being ·100 of a degree centigrade at 4° or 5° centigrade, and ·155 at temperatures of from 89° to 93° centigrade for a difference of pressure due to 100 inches of mercury.

so that temperature is changed from T to $T + \partial T$. Let this be annulled by abstraction of heat $C_p \partial T$ at constant pressure. ($C_p =$ sp. heat press. const.) [It is to be understood that dv is the total expansion existing, *after* this abstraction of heat.] The energy e of the fluid has been increased by $de = -pdv + vdp - C_p \partial T$.

Now, since the original temperature has been restored, the same expansion dv if imposed isothermally would involve the same energy change de; but in that case heat dH (dynamical) would be absorbed, and work pdv would be done by the gas. Hence $de = dH - pdv$. This, with the former value of de, gives $dH = vdp - C_p \partial T$. Thomson's work-ratio is thus $pdv / (vdp - C_p \partial T)$. Now suppose dp imposed without change of volume, and dT to be the resulting temperature change. The temperature and pressure ratios are dT/T, dp/p. Thus $dT/T = dp \, dv / (vdp - C_p \partial T)$, or

$$\frac{v}{T} \frac{dT}{dv} = \frac{1}{1 - \dfrac{C_p}{v} \dfrac{\partial T}{dp}}$$

which is Thomson's equation. The *minus* sign on the right arises from a heating effect having been taken here as the normal case.

If the temperature T is restored by removing the heat at constant volume, a similar process gives the equation

$$\frac{v}{T} \frac{dT}{dv} = \frac{1 + \dfrac{\partial T}{\partial p} \dfrac{\partial T}{dp}}{1 - \dfrac{C_v}{v} \dfrac{\partial T}{dp}}$$

where dp is the change of pressure *before* the restoration of the temperature T, and $\partial T / \partial p$ is the rate of variation of T with p, volume constant.

Elaborate discussions of the theory of this experiment will be found in modern treatises on thermodynamics, and in various recent memoirs, and the differential equation has been modified in various ways, and integrated on various suppositions, which it would be out of place to discuss here.

The cooling effect of passing a gas such as air or oxygen through a narrow orifice has been used to liquefy the gas. The stream of gas is pumped along a pipe towards the opening, and that which has passed the orifice and been slightly cooled is led on its way back to the pump along the outside of the pipe by which more gas is approaching the orifice, and so cools slightly the advancing current. The gas which emerges later is thus cooler than that which emerged before, and the process goes on until the issuing gas is liquefied and falls down into the lower part of the pipe surrounding the orifice, whence it can be drawn off into vessels constructed to receive and preserve it.

It is possible thus to liquefy hydrogen, which shows that at the low temperature at which the process is usually started (an initial cooling is applied) the passage through the orifice has a cooling effect as in the other cases.

Another idea, that of *thermodynamic motivity*, on which Thomson suggested might be founded a fruitful presentation of the subject of thermodynamics, may be mentioned here. It was set forth in a letter written to Professor Tait in May 1879. If a system of bodies be given, all at different temperatures, it is possible to reduce them to a common temperature, and by doing so to extract a certain amount of mechanical energy from them. The temperatures must for this purpose be equalised by perfect thermodynamic engines working between the final temperature T_0, say, and the temperatures of the different parts of the system. This process is one of the levelling up and the levelling down of temperature; and the temperature T_0 is such that exactly the heat given out at T_0 by certain engines, receiving heat from bodies of higher temperature than T_0, is supplied to the engines which work between T_0 and bodies at lower temperatures. The whole useful work obtained in this way was called by Thomson the *motivity* of the system. Of course equalisation of temperature may be obtained by conduction, and in this case the energy which might be utilised is lost. With two equal and similar bodies at absolute temperatures T, T' the temperature to which they are reduced when their motivity is extracted is $\sqrt{TT'}$. If the temperatures are equalised by conduction the resulting temperature is higher, being $\frac{1}{2}(T+T')$. Thus, if only the two bodies are available for engines to work between, the motivity is the measure of the energy lost when conduction brings about equalisation of temperature.

A very suggestive paper on the subject was published by Lord Kelvin in the *Trans. R.S.E.*, vol. 28, 1877-8.

DISSIPATION OF ENERGY

In connection with the theory of heat must be mentioned Thomson's great generalisation, the theory of the dissipation of energy.[1] Most people have some

[1] "On a Universal Tendency in Nature to Dissipation of Energy," *Proc. R.S.E.*, 1852, and *Phil. Mag.*, Oct. 1852.

notion of the meaning of the physical doctrine of conservation of energy, though in popular discourses it is
usually misstated. What is meant is that in a finite
material system, which is isolated in the sense that
it is not acted on by force from without, the total
amount of energy—that is, energy of motion and energy
of relative position (including energy of chemical affinity)
of the parts—remains constant. The usual misstatement is that the energy of the *universe* is constant.
This may be true if the universe is finite; if the
universe is infinite in extent the statement has no
meaning. In any case, we know nothing about the
universe as a whole, and therefore make no statements
regarding it.

But while there is thus conservation or constancy of
amount of energy in an isolated and finite material
system, this energy may to residents on the system
become unavailable. For useful work within such a
system is done by conversion of energy from one form
to another and the total amount remains unchanged.
But if this conversion is prevented all processes which
involve such conversion must cease, and among these
are vital processes.

The unavailable form which the energy of the
system with which we are directly and at present
concerned, whatever may become of us ultimately, is
taking, according to Thomson's theory, is universally
diffused heat. How this comes about may be seen as
follows. Even a perfect engine, if the refrigerator be
at the lowest available temperature, rejects a quantity
of heat which cannot be utilised for the performance of
the work. This heat is diffused by conduction and
radiation to surrounding bodies, and so to bodies more

remote, and the general temperature of the system is raised. Moreover, as heat engines are imperfect there is heat rejected to the surroundings by conduction, and produced by work done against friction, so that the heat thrown on the unavailable or waste heap is still further increased.

Conduction of heat is the great agency by which energy is more and more dispersed in this unavailable form throughout the totality of material bodies. As has been seen, available motivity is continually wasted through its agency ; and in the flow of heat in the earth and in the sun and other unequally heated bodies of our system the waste of energy is prodigious. Aided by convection currents in the air and in the ocean it continually equalises temperatures, but does so at an immense cost of useful energy.

Then in our insanely wasteful methods of heating our houses by open fires, of half burning the coal used in boiler furnaces, and allowing unconsumed carbon to escape into the atmosphere in enormous quantities, while a very large portion of the heat actually generated is allowed to escape up chimneys with heated gases, the store of unavailable heat is being added to at a rate which will entail great distress, if not ruin, on humanity at no indefinitely distant future. It will be the height of imprudence to trust to the prospect, not infrequently referred to at the present time, of drawing on the energy locked up in the atomic structure of matter. He would be a foolish man who would wastefully squander the wealth he possesses, in the belief that he can recoup himself from mines which all experience so far shows require an expenditure to work them far beyond any return that has as yet been obtained.

It is not apart from our present theme to urge that it is high time the question of the national economy of fuel, and the desirability of utilising by afforestation the solar energy continually going to waste on the surface of the earth, were dealt with by statesmen. If statesmen would but make themselves acquainted with the results of physical science in this magnificent region of cosmic economics there would be some hope, but, alas ! as a rule their education is one which inevitably leads to neglect, if not to disdain of physical teaching.

From the causes which have been referred to, energy is continually being dissipated, not destroyed, but locked up in greater and greater quantity in the general heat of bodies. There is always friction, always heat conduction and convection, so that as our stores of motional or positional energy, whether of chemical substances uncombined, the earth's motion, or what not, are drawn upon, the inevitable fraction, too often a large proportion, is shed off and the general temperature raised. After a large part of the whole existent energy has gone thus to raise the dead level of things, no difference of temperature adequate for heat engines to work between will be possible, and the inevitable death of all things will approach with headlong rapidity.

THERMOELASTICITY AND THERMOELECTRICITY

In the second definition of the scale of absolute temperature just discussed, stress of any type may be substituted for pressure, and the corresponding displacement s for the change of volume. Thus for a piece of elastic material put through a cycle of changes we may substitute dS for dp and Ads for dv; where A is such a factor that $AdSds$ is the work done in the displacement ds by the stress dS. As an example consider a wire subjected to simple longitudinal stress S. Longitudinal extension is produced, but this is not the only change; there is at the same time lateral contraction. However, s within certain limits is proportional to S.

Let heat dH in dynamical measure be given to the wire while the stress S is maintained constant, and let the extension increase from s to $s + ds$. The stress S will do work $ASds$ *on the wire*, and the work ratio will be $-ASds / dH$. Now let the stress be increased to $S + dS$ while the extension is kept constant, and the absolute temperature raised from T to $T + dT$. The stress ratio (as we may call it) is dS/S and the temperature ratio dT/T. Thus we obtain (p. 134 above)

$$-\frac{dS}{dT} = \frac{1}{TA}\frac{dH}{ds}$$

In his *Heat* article Thomson used the alteration e of strain under constant stress (that is ds/l, where l is the length of the wire) corresponding to an amount of heat sufficient to raise the temperature under constant stress by $1°$. Hence if K be the specific heat under constant stress, and le be put for ds in the sense just stated, we have

$$dT = -\frac{TedS}{K\rho} \quad . \quad . \quad . \quad (F)$$

where ρ is the density, since $dH = K\rho l A$.

The ratio of dH to the increase ds of the extension is positive or negative, that is, the substance absorbs or evolves heat, when strained under the condition of constant stress, according as dS/dT is negative or positive. Or we may put the same thing in another way which is frequently useful. If a wire subjected to constant stress has heat given to it, ds is negative or positive, in other words the wire shortens or lengthens, according as dS/dT is positive or negative, that is, according as the stress for a given strain is increased or diminished by increase of temperature.

It is known from experiment that a metal wire expands under constant stress when heat is given to it, and thus we learn from the equation (F) that the stress required for a given strain is diminished when the temperature of the wire is raised. Again, a strip of india-rubber stretched by a weight is shortened if its temperature is raised, consequently the stress required for a given strain is increased by rise of temperature.

These results, from a qualitative point of view, are self-evident. But from what has been set forth it will be obvious that an equation exactly similar to (F) holds whether the change ds of s is taken as before under constant stress, or at uniform temperature, or whether the change dS of S is effected adiabatically or at constant strain.

In all these cases the same equation

$$dT = -\ T\frac{edS}{K\rho} \quad . \quad . \quad . \quad \text{(G)}$$

applies, with the change of meaning of dT involved.

This equation differs from that of Thomson as given in various places (*e. g.* in the *Encyclopædia Britannica* article on *Elasticity* which he also wrote) in the negative sign on the right-hand side, but the difference is only apparent. According to his specification a *pressure* would be a positive stress, and an *expansion* a positive displacement, and in applying the equation to numerical examples this must be borne in mind so that the proper signs may be given to each numerical magnitude. As an example of adiabatic change, a sudden extension of the wire already referred to by an increase of stress dS may be considered. If there is not time for the passage of heat from or to the surroundings of the wire, the change of temperature will be given by equation (G).

This equation was applied by Thomson (article *Elasticity*) to find the relation between what he called the kinetic modulus of elasticity and the static modulus, that is, between the modulus for adiabatic strain and the modulus for isothermal strain.

The augmentation of the strain produced by raising the temperature $1°$ is e, and therefore edT, that is, $-Te^2dS/K\rho$, is the increase of strain due to the sudden rise of temperature dT. This added to the isothermal strain produced by dS will give the whole adiabatic strain. Thus if M be the static or isothermal modulus, the adiabatic strain is $dS/M - Te^2dS/K\rho$. If M' denote the kinetic or adiabatic modulus its value is dS divided by the whole adiabatic strain, that is, $M' = M/(1 - MTe^2/K\rho)$ and the ratio $M'/M = 1/(1 - MTe^2/K\rho)$.

It is well known and easy to prove, without the use of any theorem which can be properly called thermodynamic, that this ratio of moduli is equal to the ratio of the specific heat K of the substance, under the condition of constant stress, to the specific heat N under the condition of constant strain of the corresponding type. This, indeed, is self-evident if two changes of stress, one isothermal the other adiabatic, *which produce the same steps of displacement ds*, be considered, and it be remembered that the step ∂T of temperature which accompanies the adiabatic change may be regarded as made up of a step $- dT$ of temperature, accompanying a displacement *ds* effected at constant stress, and then two successive steps dT and ∂T effected, at constant strain, along with the steps of stress dS. The ratio M'/M is easily seen to have the value $(\partial T + dT) / dt$, and since $- KdT + N (\partial T + dT) = 0$, by the adiabatic condition, the theorem is proved.

Laplace's celebrated result for air, according to which the adiabatic bulk-modulus is equal to the static bulk-modulus multiplied by the ratio of the specific heat of air pressure constant to the specific heat of air volume constant, is a particular example of this theory.

Thomson showed in the *Elasticity* article how, by the value of M'/M, derived as above from thermo-dynamic theory, the value of K/N could be obtained for different substances and for different types of stress, and gave very interesting tables of results for solids, liquids, and gases subjected to pressure-stress (bulk-modulus) and for solids subjected to longitudinal stress (Young's modulus).

The discussion as to the relation of the adiabatic and isothermal moduli of elasticity is part of a very important paper on " Thermoelastic, Thermomagnetic, and Thermoelectric Properties of Matter," which he published in the *Philosophical Magazine* for January 1878. This was in the main a reprint of an article entitled, " On the Thermoelastic and Thermomagnetic

Properties of Matter, Part I," which appeared in April 1855 in the first number of the *Quarterly Journal of Mathematics*. Only thermoelasticity was considered in this article; the thermomagnetic results had, however, been indicated in an article on "Thermomagnetism" in the second edition of the *Cyclopædia of Physical Science*, edited and in great part written by Professor J. P. Nichol, and published in 1860. For the same *Cyclopædia* Thomson also wrote an article entitled, "Thermo-electric, Division I.—Pyro-Electricity, or Thermo-Electricity of Non-conducting Crystals," and the enlarged *Phil. Mag.* article also contained the application of thermodynamics to this kind of thermo-electric action.

This great paper cannot be described without a good deal of mathematical analysis; but the student who has read the earlier thermodynamical papers of Thomson will have little difficulty in mastering it. It must suffice to say here that it may be regarded as giving the keynote of much of the general thermodynamic treatment of physical phenomena, which forms so large a part of the physical mathematics of the present day, and which we owe to Willard Gibbs Duhem, and other contemporary writers.

Thomson had, however, previous to the publication of this paper, applied thermodynamic theory to thermo-electric phenomena. A long series of papers containing experimental investigations, and entitled, "Electrodynamic Qualities of Metals," are placed in the second volume of his *Mathematical and Physical Papers*. This series begins with the Bakerian Lecture (published in the *Transactions of the Royal Society* for 1856) which includes an account of the remarkable experimental work accomplished during the preceding four or five years by the volunteer laboratory corps in the newly-established physical laboratory in the old College. The subjects dealt with are the Electric Convection of Heat, Thermoelectric Inversions, the Effects of Mechanical Strain and of Magnetisation on the Thermoelectric Qualities of Metals, and the Effects of Tension and Magnetisation on the Electric Conductivity of Metals. It is only possible to give here a very short indication of the thermodynamic treatment, and of the nature of Thomson's remarkable discovery of the electric convection of heat.

It was found by Seebeck in 1822 that when a circuit is formed of two different metals (without any cell or battery) a current flows round the circuit if the two junctions are not at the same temperature. For example, if the two metals be rods of antimony and bismuth, joined at their extremities so as to form a complete circuit, and one junction be warmed while the other is kept at the ordinary temperature, a current flows across the hot junction in the direction from bismuth to antimony. Similarly, if a circuit be made of a copper wire and an iron wire, a current passes across the warmer junction from copper to iron. The current strength—other things being the same—depends on the metals used ; for example, bismuth and antimony are more effective than other metals.

It was found by Peltier that when a current, say from a battery, is sent round such a circuit, that junction is cooled and that junction is heated by the passage of the current, which, being respectively heated and cooled, would without the cell have caused a current to flow in the same direction. Thus the current produced by the difference of temperature of the junctions causes an absorption of heat from the warmer junction, and an evolution of heat at the colder junction.

This naturally suggested to Thomson the consideration of a circuit of two metals, with the junctions at different temperatures, as a heat engine, of which the hot junction was the source and the cold junction the refrigerator, while the heat generated in the circuit by the current and other work performed, if there was any, was the equivalent of the difference between the heat absorbed and the heat evolved. Of course in such an arrangement there is always irreversible loss of heat by conduction ; but when such losses are properly allowed for the circuit is capable of being correctly regarded as a reversible engine.

Shortly after Seebeck's discovery it was found by Cumming that when the hot junction was increased in temperature the electromotive force increased more and more slowly, at a certain temperature of the hot junction took its maximum value, and then as the temperature of the hot junction was further increased began to diminish, and ultimately, at a sufficiently high temperature, in most instances changed sign. The temperature of maximum electromotive force was found to be independent of the temperature of the colder junction. It is called the temperature of the neutral point, from the fact that if the two junctions of a thermoelectric circuit be kept at a constant small difference of temperature, and be both raised in temperature until one is at a higher temperature than the neutral point, and the other is at a lower, the electromotive force will fall off, until finally, when this point is reached, it has become zero.

Thus it was found that for every pair of metals there was at least one such temperature of the hot junction, and it was assumed, with consequences in agreement with experimental results, that when the temperature was the neutral temperature there was neither absorption nor evolution of heat at the junction. But then the source provided by the thermodynamic view just stated had ceased to exist. The current still flowed, there was evolution of heat at the cold junction, and likewise Joulean evolution of heat in the wires of the circuit in consequence of their resistance. Hence it was clear that energy must be obtained elsewhere than at the junctions. Thomson solved the problem by showing that (besides the Joulean evolution of heat) there is absorption (or evolution) of heat when a current flows in a conductor along which there is a gradient of temperature. For example, when an electric current flows along an unequally heated copper wire, heat is evolved where the current flows from the hot parts to the cold, and heat is absorbed where the flow is from cold to hot. When the hot junction is at the temperature of zero absorption or evolution of heat—the so-called neutral temperature—the heat absorbed in the flow of the circuit along the unequally heated conductors is greater than that evolved on the whole, by an amount which is the equivalent of the energy electrically expended in the circuit in the same time.

It was found, moreover, that the amount of heat absorbed by a given current in ascending or descending through a given difference of temperature is different in different metals. When the current was unit current and the temperature difference also unity,

Thomson called the heat absorbed or evolved in a metal the specific heat of electricity in the metal, a name which is convenient in some ways, but misleading in others. The term rather conveys the notion that electricity has a material existence. A substance such as copper, lead, water, or mercury has a specific heat in a perfectly understood sense ; electricity is not a substance, hence there cannot be in the same proper sense a specific heat of electricity.

However, this absorption and evolution of heat was investigated experimentally and mathematically by Thomson, and is generally now referred to in thermo-electric discussions as the " Thomson effect."

Part VI (*Trans. R.S.*, 1875) of the investigations of the electrodynamic qualities of metals dealt with the effects of stretching and compressing force, and of torsion, on the magnetisation of iron and steel and of nickel and cobalt.

One of the principal results was the discovery that the effect of longitudinal pull is to increase the inductive magnetisation of soft iron, and of transverse thrust to diminish it, so long as the magnetising field does not exceed a certain value. When this value, which depends on the specimen, is exceeded, the effect of stress is reversed. The field-intensity at which the effect is reversed is called the Villari critical intensity, from the fact, afterwards ascertained, that the result had previously been established by Villari in Italy. No such critical value of the field was found to exist for steel, or nickel, or cobalt.

In some of the experiments the specimen was put through a cycle of magnetic changes, and the results recorded by curves. These proved that in going from

one state to another and returning the material lagged
in its return path behind the corresponding states in
the outward path. This is the phenomenon called
later "hysteresis," and studied in minute detail by
Ewing and others. Thomson's magnetic work was
thus the starting point of many more recent researches.

CHAPTER IX

THOMSON devoted great attention from time to time
to the science of hydrodynamics. This is perhaps
the most abstruse subject in the domain of applied
mathematics, and when viscosity (the frictional resistance to the relative motion of particles of the fluid)
is taken into account, passes beyond the resources of
mathematical science in its present state of development. But leaving viscosity entirely aside, and dealing
only with so-called perfect fluids, the difficulties are
often overwhelming. For a long time the only kind
of fluid motion considered was, with the exception of
a few simple cases, that which is called irrotational
motion. This motion is characterised by the analytical
peculiarity, that the velocity of an element of the fluid
in any direction is the rate of variation per unit distance
in that direction of a function of the coordinates (the
distances which specify the position) of the particle.
This condition very much simplifies the analysis ; but
when it does not hold we have much more serious
difficulties to overcome. Then the elements of the
fluid have what is generally, but quite improperly,
called molecular rotation. For we know little of the
molecules of a fluid ; even when we deal with infinitesimal elements, in the analysis of fluid motion, we are

considering the fluid in mass. But what is meant
is elemental rotation, a rotation of the infinitesimal
elements as they move. We have an example of such
motion in the air when a ring of smoke escapes from
the funnel of a locomotive or the lips of a tobacco-
smoker, in the motion of part of the liquid when a cup
of tea is stirred by drawing the spoon from one side to
the other, or when the blade of an oar is moving
through the water. In these last two cases the de-
pressions seen in the surface are the ends of a vortex
which extends between them and terminates on the
surface. In all these examples what have been called
vortices are formed, and hence the name vortex motion
has been given to all those cases in which the condition
of irrotationality is not satisfied.

The first great paper on vortex motion was published
by von Helmholtz in 1858, and ten years later a
memoir on the same subject by Thomson was published in the *Transactions of the Royal Society of
Edinburgh*. In that memoir are given very much
simpler proofs of von Helmholtz's main theorems, and,
moreover, some new theorems of wide application to
the motion of fluids. One of these is so comprehensive that it may be said with truth to contain the
whole of the dynamics of a perfect fluid. We go on
to indicate the contents of the principal papers, as far
as that can be done without the introduction of analysis
of a difficult description.

In Chapter VI reference has been made to the
"Notes on Hydrodynamics" published by Thomson
in the *Cambridge and Dublin Mathematical Journal*
for 1848 and 1849. These Notes were not intended
to be entirely original, but were composed for the

use of students, like Airy's *Tracts* of fifteen years before.

The first Note dealt with the equation of continuity, that is to say, the mathematical expression of the obvious fact that if any region of space in a moving fluid be considered, the excess of rate of flow into the space across the bounding surface, above the rate of flow out, is equal to the rate of growth of the quantity of fluid within the space. The proof given is that now usually repeated in text-books of hydrodynamics.

The second Note discussed the condition fulfilled at the bounding surface of a moving fluid. The chief mathematical result is the equation which expresses the fact, also obvious without analysis, that there is no flow of the fluid across the surface. In other words, the component of the motion of a fluid particle in the immediate neighbourhood of the surface at any instant, taken in the direction perpendicular to the surface, must be equal to the motion of the surface in that direction at the same instant.

The third Note, published a year later (February 1849), is of considerable scientific importance. It is entitled, "On the Vis Viva of a Liquid in Motion." What used to be called the "vis viva" of a body is double what is now called the energy of motion, or kinetic energy, of the body. The term liquid is merely a brief expression for a fluid, the mass of which per unit volume is the same throughout, and suffers no variation. The fluid, moreover, is supposed devoid of friction, that is, the relative motions of its parts are unresisted by tangential force between them. The chief theorem proved and discussed may be described as follows.

The liquid is supposed to fill the space within a closed envelope, which fulfils the condition of being "simply continuous." The condition will be understood by imagining any two points A, B, within the space, to be joined by two lines ACB, ADB both lying within the space. These two lines will form a circuit $ACBDA$. If now this circuit, however it may be drawn, can be contracted down to a point, without any part of the circuit passing out of the space, the condition is fulfilled. Clearly the space within the surface of an anchor-ring, or a curtain-ring, would not fulfil this condition, for one part of the circuit might pass from A to B round the ring one way, and the other from A to B the other way. The circuit could not then be contracted towards a point without passing out of the ring.

Now let the liquid given at rest in such a space be set in motion by any arbitrarily specified variation of position of the envelope. The liquid within will be set in motion in a manner depending entirely on the motion of the envelope. It is possible to conceive of other motions of the liquid than that taken, which all agree in having the specified motion of the surface. Thomson's theorem asserts that the motion actually taken has less kinetic energy than that of any of the other motions which have the same motion of the bounding surface.

The motion produced has the property described by the word "irrotational," that is, the elements of the fluid have no spinning motion—they move without rotation. A small portion of a fluid may describe any path—may go round in a circle, for example—and yet have no rotation. The reader may imagine a ball carried round in a circle, but in such a way that no line in the body ever changes its direction. The body has translation, but no spin.

Irrotationality of a fluid is secured, as stated above, when the velocity of each element in any direction is the rate of variation per unit distance in that direction of a certain function of the coordinates, the distances, taken parallel to three lines perpendicular to one another and drawn from a point, which specify the position of the particle. In fact, what is called a velocity-potential exists, similar to the potential described in Chapter IV above, for an electric field. This condition, together with the specified motion of the surface, suffices to determine the motion of the fluid.

Two important particular consequences were pointed out by Thomson : (1) that the motion of the fluid at any instant depends solely on the form and motion of the bounding surface, and is therefore independent of the previous motion ; and (2) that if the bounding surface be instantaneously brought to rest, the liquid throughout the vessel will also be instantly brought to rest.

This theorem was afterwards generalised by Thomson (*Proc. R.S.E.*, 1863), and applied to any material system of connected particles set into motion by specified velocities simultaneously and suddenly imposed at selected points of the system. It was already known that the kinetic energy of a system of bodies connected in any manner, and set in motion by impulses applied at specified points, was either a maximum or a minimum, as compared with that for any other motion compatible with these impulses, and with the connections of the system. This was proved by Lagrange in the *Mécanique Analytique* as a generalisation of a theorem given by Euler for a rigid body set into rotation by an impulse.

Bertrand proved in 1842 that when the impulses applied are given in amount, and are applied at specified points, the system starts off with kinetic energy greater than that of any other motion which is consistent with the given impulses and the connections of the system. This other motion must be such as could be produced in the system by the given impulses, together with any other set of impulses capable of doing no work on the whole.

Thomson's theorem is curiously complementary to Bertrand's. Let the system be acted on by impulses applied at certain specified points, and by no other impulses of any kind ; and let the impulses be such as to start those selected points with any prescribed velocities. The system will start off with kinetic energy which is less than that of any other motion which the system could have consistently with the prescribed velocities, and which it could be constrained to take by impulses which do no work on the whole. In each case the difference of energies is the energy of the motion which must be compounded with one motion to give the other which is compared with it.

A simple example, such as might be taken of the particular case considered by Euler, may help to make these theorems clear. Imagine a straight uniform rod to lie on a horizontal table, between which and the rod there is no friction. Let the rod be struck a blow at one end in a horizontal direction at right angles to the length of the rod. If no other impulse acts, the end of the rod will move off with a certain definite velocity, and the other parts of the rod (which is supposed perfectly unbending) will be started by the connections of the system. It is obvious that any number of other motions of the rod can be imagined, all of which give the same motion of the extremity struck. But the actual motion taken is one of turning about that point of the rod which is two-thirds of the length from the end struck. If the reader will consider the kinetic energy for any other horizontal turning motion consistent with the same motion of the end, he will find that the kinetic energy is greater than that of the motion just specified. This motion could be produced by applying at the point about which the rod turns the impulse required to keep that point at rest. The impulse so applied would do no work. The actual value is $\frac{1}{8}mv^2$, where m denotes the mass of the rod and v the velocity of the end. If the motion taken were one of rotation about a point of the rod at distance x from the end struck, the kinetic energy would be $m(4l^2 - 6lx + 3x^2)v^2 / 6x^2$, where $2l$ is the length of the rod, and this has its least value $\frac{1}{8}mv^2$ for $x = 4l/3$. For example, $x = 2l$ gives $\frac{1}{6}mv^2$, which is greater than the value just found.

Bertrand's theorem applied to this case of motion is not quite so easy, perhaps, to understand. The motion which is said to have maximum energy is one given by a specified impulse at the end struck, and this, in the absence of any other impulses, would be a motion of minimum energy. But let the alternative motion, which is to be compared with that actually taken, be one constrained by additional impulses such as can together effect no work, and the existence of the maximum is accounted for. The kinetic energy produced is one-half the product of the impulse into the velocity of the point struck, that is $\frac{1}{2}Iv$, and it has just been seen that this is the product of $\frac{1}{6}mv^2$ by the factor $(4l^2 - 6lx + 3x^2)/x^2$. This factor is $3l/mv$, and is a minimum when $x = 4l/3$. Thus for a given I, v will have its maximum value when the factor referred to is least, and $\frac{1}{2}Iv$ will then be a maximum.

The bar can be constrained to turn about another point by a fixed pivot there situated. An impulse will be applied to the rod by the pivot, simultaneously with the blow ; and it is obvious that this impulse does no work, since there is no displacement of the point to which it is applied.

The two theorems are consequences of one principle. The constraint in each case increases what may be called the effective inertia, which may be taken as I/v. Thus when v is given, I is increased by any constraint compelling the rod to rotate about a particular axis, and so $\frac{1}{2}Iv$, or the kinetic energy, is increased. On the other hand, when I is given the same constraint diminishes v, and so $\frac{1}{2}Iv$ is diminished.

A short paper published in the B. A. Report for 1852 points out that the lines of force near a small magnet, placed with its axis along the lines of force in a uniform magnetic field, as it would rest under the action of the field, are at corresponding points similar to those of the field of an insulated spherical conductor, under the inductive influence of a distant electric change. Further, the fact is noted that, if the magnet be oppositely directed to the field, the lines of force are curved outwards, just as the lines of flow of a uniform stream would be by a spherical obstacle, at the surface of which no eddies were caused.   This is one of those instructive analogies between the theory of fluid motion and other theories involving perfectly analogous fundamental ideas, which Thomson was fond of pointing out, and which helped him in his repeated attempts to imagine mechanical representations of physical phenomena of different kinds.

With these may be placed another, which in lectures he frequently dwelt on—a simple doublet, as it is called, consisting of a point-source of fluid and an equal and closely adjacent point-sink.   A short tube in an infinite mass of liquid, which is continually flowing in at one end and out at the other, may serve as a realisation of this arrangement.   The lines of flow outside the tube are exactly analogous to the lines of force of a small magnet ; and if at the same time there exist a uniform flow of the liquid in the direction of the length of the tube, the field of flow will be an exact picture of the field of force of the small magnet, when it is placed with its length along the lines of a previously existing uniform field.   The flow in the doublet will be with or against the general flow according as the magnet is directed with or against the field.

The paper on vortex-motion has been referred to above, and an indication given of the nature of the fluid-motion described by this title.   There are, how-ever, two cases of fluid-motion which are referred to as vortices, though the fundamental criterion of vortex-motion—the non-existence of a velocity-potential—is satisfied in only one of them.   The exhibition of one of these was a favourite experiment in Thomson's ordinary lectures, as his old students will remember.

If water in a large bowl is stirred rapidly with a teaspoon carried round and round in a circle about the axis of the bowl, the surface will become concave, and the form of the central part will be a paraboloid of revolution about the vertical through the lowest point, that is to say, any section of that part of the surface made by a vertical plane containing the axis will be a parabola symmetrical about the axis. The motion can be better produced by mounting the vessel on a whirling-table, and rotating it about the vertical axis coinciding with its axis of figure; but the phenomenon can be quite well seen without this machinery. In this case the velocity of each particle of the water is proportional to its distance from the axis, and the whole mass, when relative equilibrium is set up, turns, as if it were rigid, about the axis of the vessel. Each element of the fluid in this "forced vortex," as it is called, is in rotation, and, like the moon, makes one turn in one revolution about the centre of its path. This is, therefore, a true, though very simple, case of vortex-motion.

On the other hand, what may be called a "free vortex" may exist, and is approximated to sometimes when water in a vessel is allowed to run off through an escape pipe at the bottom. The velocity of an element in this "vortex" is inversely proportional to its distance from the centre, and the form of the free surface is quite different from that in the other case. The name "free vortex" is often given to this case of motion, but there is no vortex-motion about it whatever.

Thomson's great paper on vortex-motion was read before the Royal Society of Edinburgh in 1867, and was recast and augmented in the following year. It will be possible to give here only a sketch of its scope and main results.

The fluid is supposed contained in a closed fixed vessel which is either simply or multiply continuous (see p. 156), and may contain immersed in it simply or multiply continuous solids. When these solids exist their surfaces are part of the boundary of the liquid ; they are surrounded by the liquid unless they are anywhere in contact with the containing vessel, and their density is supposed to be the same as that of the liquid. They may be acted on by forces from without, and they act on the liquid with pressure-forces, and either directly or through the liquid on one another.

The first result obtained is fairly obvious. The centre of mass of the whole system must remain at rest whatever external forces act on the solids, since the density is the same everywhere within the vessel, and the vessel is fixed ; that is to say, there is no momentum of the contents of the vessel in any direction. For whatever motion of the solids is set up by the external forces, must be accompanied by a motion of the liquid, equal and opposite in the sense here indicated.

After a discussion of what he calls the impulse of the motion, which is the system of impulsive forces on the movable solids which would generate the motion from rest, Thomson proceeds to prove the important proposition that the rotational motion of every portion of the liquid mass, if it is zero at any one instant for every portion of the mass, remains always zero. This is done by considering the angular momentum of any small spherical portion of the liquid relatively to an

axis through the centre of the sphere, and proving that
in order that it may vanish, for every axis, the component velocities of the fluid at the centre must be
derivable from a velocity-potential. The angular
momentum of a particle about an axis is the product of the component of the particle's momentum,
at right angles to the plane through the particle and
the axis, by the distance of the particle from the axis.
The sum of all such products for the particles making
up the body (when proper account is taken of the
signs according to the direction of turning round the
axis) is the angular momentum. The proof of this
result adopted is due to Stokes. The angular velocities
of an element of fluid at a point x, y, z, about the axes
of x, y, z are shown to be $\frac{1}{2}(\partial w / \partial y - \partial v / \partial z)$, etc.

The condition was therefore shown to be necessary ;
it remained to prove that it was sufficient. This is
obvious at once from the definition of the velocity-
potential, which must now be supposed to exist in
order that its sufficiency may be proved. If any
diameter of the spherical portion be taken as the axis,
and any plane through that axis be considered, the
velocity of a particle at right angles to that plane can
be at once expressed as the rate at which the velocity-
potential varies per unit distance along the circle,
symmetrical about the axis, on which the particle lies.
The integral of the velocity-potential round this circle
vanishes, and so the angular momentum for any thin
uniform ring of particles about the axis also vanishes,
and as the sphere is made up of such rings, the whole
angular momentum is zero. Thus the condition is
sufficient.

Thomson then proves that if the angular momentum

thus considered be zero for every portion of the liquid at any one instant, it remains zero at every subsequent instant ; that is, no physical action whatsoever could set up angular momentum within the fluid, which, it is to be remembered, is supposed to be frictionless. The proof here given cannot be sketched because it depends on the differential equation of continuity satisfied by the velocity-potential throughout the fluid (the same differential equation, in fact, that is satisfied by the distribution of temperature in a uniform conducting medium in the stationary state), and the consequent expression of this function for any spherical space in the fluid as a series of spherical harmonic functions. To a reader to whom the properties of these functions are known the process can present no difficulty.

An entirely different proof of this proposition is given subsequently in the paper, and depends on a new and very general theorem, which has been described as containing almost the whole theory of the motion of a fluid. This depends on what Thomson called the flow along any path joining any two points P, Q in the fluid. Let q be the velocity of the fluid at any element of length ds of such a path, and θ be the angle between the direction of ds (taken positive in the sense from P to Q) and the direction of q: $q \cos \theta . ds$ is the flow along ds. If u, v, w be the components of q at ds, parallel to the axes, and dx, dy, dz be the projections of ds on the axes, $udx + vdy + wdz$ is the same thing as $q \cos \theta . ds$. The sum of the values of either of these expressions for all the elements of the path between P and Q is the flow along the path. The statement that u, v, w are the space-rates of variation of a function ϕ (of x, y, z) parallel to the axes, or that $q \cos \theta$ is the space-rate of variation of ϕ along ds, merely means that this sum is the same for whatever path may be drawn from P to Q. This, however, is only the case when the paths are so taken that in each case the value of ϕ returns after variation along a closed path to the value which it had at the starting point, that is, the closed path must be capable of being contracted to a point without passing out of space occupied by irrotationally moving fluid.

Since the flow from P to Q is the same for any two paths which fulfil this condition, the flow from P to Q by any one path and from Q to P by any other must be zero. The flow round such a closed path is not zero if the condition is not fulfilled, and its value was called by Thomson the circulation round the path.

The general theorem which he established may now be stated. Consider any path joining PQ, and moving with the fluid, so that the line contains always the same fluid particles. Let $\dot{u}, \dot{v}, \dot{w}$ be the time-rates of change of u, v, w at an element ds of the path, at any instant, and du, dv, dw the excesses of the values of u, v, w at the terminal extremity of ds above the values at the other extremity ; then the time-rate of variation of $udx + vdy + wdz$ is $\dot{u}dx + \dot{v}dy + \dot{w}dz + udu + vdv + wdw$ or $\dot{u}dx + \dot{v}dy + \dot{w}dz + qdq$, where q has the meaning specified above. Thus if S be the flow for the whole path PQ, and $\dot{S}$ its time-rate of variation, S' denote the sum of $\dot{u}dx + \dot{v}dy + \dot{w}dz$ along the path from P to Q, and q_1, q_0 the resultant fluid velocities at Q and P, we get $\dot{S} = S' + \frac{1}{2}(q_1^2 - q_0^2)$. This is Thomson's theorem. If the curve be closed, that is, if P and Q be coincident, $q_1 = q_0$ and $\dot{S} = S'$. But in certain circumstances S' is zero, and so therefore is also $\dot{S}$. Thus in the circumstances referred to, as the closed path moves with the fluid $\dot{S}$ is continually zero, and it follows that if $\dot{S}$ is zero at any instant it remains zero ever after. But $\dot{S}$ is only zero if u, v, w are derivable from a potential, single valued in the space in which the closed path is drawn, so that the path could be shrunk down to a point without ever passing out of such space. In a perfect fluid if this condition is once fulfilled for a closed curve moving with the fluid, it is fulfilled for this curve ever after.

The circumstances in which S' is zero are these :— the external force, per unit mass, acting on the fluid at any point is to be derivable from a potential-function, and the density of the fluid is to be a function of the pressure (also a function of the coordinates) ; and these functions must be such as to render S' always zero for the closed path. This condition is manifestly fulfilled in many important cases ; for example, the forces are derivable from a potential due to actions, such as gravity, the origin of which is external to the fluid ; and the density is a function of the pressure (in the present case it is a constant), such that the part of S' which depends on pressure and density vanishes for the circuit.

It is to be clearly understood that the motion of a fluid may be irrotational although the value of S does not vanish for *every* closed path that can be drawn in it. The fluid may occupy multiply continuous space, and the path may or may not be drawn so that S shall be zero ; but what is necessary for irrotational motion within any space is that S should vanish for all paths which are capable of being shrunk down to zero without passing out of that space. S need not vanish for a path which cannot be so shrunk down, but it must, if the

condition just stated is fulfilled, have the same value
for any two paths, one of which can be made to pass
into the other by change of position without ever passing in whole or in part out of the space. The potential
is always single valued in fluid filling a singly continuous space such as that within a spherical shell, or between
two concentric shells ; within a hollow anchor-ring
the potential, though it exist, and the motion be irrotational, is not single valued. In the latter case the
motion is said to be *cyclic*, in the former *acyclic*.

A number of consequences are deduced from this
theorem ; and from these the properties of vortices,
which had previously been discovered by von Helmholtz,
immediately follow. First take any surface whatever
which has for bounding edge a closed curve drawn in
the fluid, and draw from any element of this surface,
of area dS, a line perpendicular to the surface towards
the side chosen as the positive side, and calculate the
angular velocity ω, say, of the fluid about that normal
from the components of angular velocity determined in
the manner explained at p. 164. This Thomson
called the *rotation* of the element. Now take the product ωdS for the surface element. It is easy to see that
this is equal to half the circulation round the bounding
edge of the element. As the fluid composing the
element moves the area dS may change, but the circulation round its edge by Thomson's theorem remains
unaltered. Thus ω alters in the inverse ratio of dS,
and the line drawn at right angles to the surface at dS,
if kept of length proportional to ω, will lengthen or
shorten as dS contracts or expands.

Now sum the values of ωdS for the finite surface
enclosed by the bounding curve. It follows from the

fact that ωdS is equal to half the circulation round the edge of dS, that this sum, which is usually denoted by $\Sigma\omega dS$, is equal to half the circulation round the closed curve which forms the edge of the surface. Also as the fluid moves the circulation round the edge remains unaltered, and therefore so does also $\Sigma\omega dS$ for the elements enclosed by it. It is important to notice that this sum being determined by the circulation in the bounding curve is the same for all surfaces which have the same boundary.

The equality of $2\Sigma\omega dS$ for the surface to the circulation round its edge was expressed by Thomson as an analytical theorem of integration, which was first given by Stokes in a Smith's Prize paper set in 1854. It is here stated, apparently by an oversight, that it was first given in Thomson and Tait's *Natural Philosophy*, § 190. In the second edition of the *Natural Philosophy* the theorem is attributed to Stokes. It is now well known as Stokes's theorem connecting a certain surface integral with a line integral, and has many applications both in physics and in geometry.

Now consider the resultant angular velocity at any point of the fluid, and draw a short line through that point in the direction of the axis of rotation. That line may be continued from point to point, and will coincide at every one of its points with the direction of the axis of rotation there. Such an axial curve, as it may be called, it is clear moves with the fluid. For take any infinitesimal area containing an element of the line ; the circulation round the edge of this area is zero, since there is no rotation about a line perpendicular to the area. Hence the circulation along the axial curve is zero, and the axial curves move with the fluid.

Take now any small plane area dS moving with the
fluid, and draw axial lines through every point of its
boundary. These will form an axial tube enclosing
dS. If θ be the angle between the direction of resultant rotation and a perpendicular to dS, the cross-section
of the tube at right angles to the normal, and to the
axial lines which bound it, is $dS \cdot \cos \theta$. Let these
axial lines be continued in both directions from the
element dS. They will enclose a tube of varying
normal cross-section ; but the product of rotation and
area of normal cross-section has everywhere the same
value. A vortex-tube with the fluid within it is called
a vortex-filament.

It will be seen that this vortex-tube must be endless,
that is, it must either return into itself, or be infinitely
long in one or both directions. For if it were terminated anywhere within the fluid, it would be possible to
form a surface, starting from a closed circuit round the
tube, continued along the surface of the tube to the
termination, and then closed by a cap situated beyond
the termination. At no part of this surface would
there be any rotation, and $\Sigma_\omega dS$, which is equal to
the circulation, would be zero for it ; and of course
this cannot be the case. Thus the tube cannot terminate within the fluid. It can, however, have both of its
ends on the surface, or one on the bounding surface
and the other at infinity, if the fluid is infinitely
extended in one direction, but in that case the termination is only apparent. The section is widened out at
the surface ; some of the bounding lines pass across
to the other apparent termination, when it also
lies on the surface, while the other lines pass off to
infinity along the surface, and correspond to other lines

coming in from infinity to the other termination. Whether the surface is infinite or not, the vortex is spread out into what is called a vortex-sheet, that is, in a surface on the two sides of which the fluid moves with different tangential velocities.

Through a vortex-ring or tube, the fluid circulates in closed lines of flow, each one of which is laced through the tube. The circulation along every line of flow which encloses the same system of vortex-tubes has the same value.

If any surface be drawn cutting a vortex-tube, it is clear from the definition of the tube that the value of $\Sigma \omega dS$ for every such surface must be the same. This Thomson calls the "rotation of the tube."

As was pointed out first by von Helmholtz, vortex-filaments correspond to circuits carrying currents and the velocity in the surrounding fluid to magnetic field-intensity. The "rotation of the tube" corresponds to the strength of the current, and sources and sinks to positive and negative magnetic poles. Thomson made great use of this analogy in his papers on electro-magnetism.

Examples of vortex-tubes are indicated on p. 154 ; and the reader may experiment with vortices in liquids with water in a tea-cup, or in a river or pond, at pleasure. Air vortices may be experimentally studied by means of a simple apparatus devised by Professor Tait, which may be constructed by anyone.

In one end of a packing-box, about 2 ft. long by 18 in. wide and 18 in. deep, a circular hole is cut, and the edges of the hole are thinned down to a blunt edge. This can be closed at pleasure by a piece of board. The opposite end is removed, and a sheet of canvas stretched tightly in its place, and tacked to the ends of the sides. Through two holes bored in one of the sides the mouths of two flasks with bent necks protrude into the box. One of these flasks contains ammonia, the other hydrochloric acid. When the hole at one end is closed up by a slip of tinplate, and the liquids are heated with a spirit-lamp, the vapours form a cloud of sal-ammoniac within the box, which is retained during its formation. The hole is then opened, and the canvas struck smartly with the palm of the open hand. Immediately a beautiful ring of

FIG. 13.

smoke emerges, clear-cut and definite as a solid, and moves across the room. (See Fig. 13.) Of course, it is a ring of air, made visible by the smoke carried with it. By varying the shape of the aperture—for example, by using instead of the hole cut in the wood, a slide of tinplate with an elliptic hole cut in it—the vortex-rings can be set in vibration as they are created, and the vibrations studied as the vortex moves.

Still more beautiful vortices can be formed in water by using a long tank of clear water to replace the air in which the vortex moves, and a compartment at one end filled with water coloured with aniline, instead of the smoke-box. A hole in the dividing partition enables the vortex to be formed, and a piston arrangement fitted to the opposite side enables the impulse to the water to be given from without.

From the account of the nature of vortex-motion given above, it will be clear that vortices in a perfect fluid once existent must be ever existent. To create a vortex within a mass of irrotationally moving perfect fluid is physically impossible. It occurred to Thomson, therefore, that ordinary matter might be portions of a perfect fluid, filling all space, differentiated from the surrounding fluid by the rotation which they possess. Such matter would fulfil the law of conservation, as it could neither be created nor destroyed by any physical act.

The results of such experiments led Thomson to frame his famous vortex-atom theory of matter, a theory, however, which he felt ultimately was beset with so many difficulties as to be unworkable.

The paper on vortex-motion also deals with the modification of Green's celebrated theorem of analysis, which, it was pointed out by Helmholtz, was necessary to adapt it to a space which is multiply continuous. The theorem connects a certain volume-integral taken throughout a closed space with an integral taken over the bounding surface of the space. This arises from the fact noticed above that in multiply continuous space (for example, the space within an endless tube) the functions which are the subject of integration may not be single valued. Such a function would be the velocity-potential for fluid circulating round the tube —cyclic motion, as it was called by Thomson. If a closed path of any form be drawn in such a tube, starting from a point P, and doubling back so as to return to P without making the circuit of the tube, the velocity-potential will vary along the tube, but will finally return to its original value when the starting point is reached. And the circulation round this circuit will be zero. But if the closed path make the circuit of the tube, the velocity-potential will continuously vary along the path, until finally, when P is reached again, the value of the function is greater (or less) than the value assumed for the starting point, by a certain definite amount which is the same for every circuit of the space. If the path be carried twice round in the same direction, the change of the function will be twice this amount, and so on. The space within a single endless tube such as an anchor-ring is doubly continuous; but much more complicated cases can be imagined. For example, an anchor-ring with a cross-connecting tube from one side to the other would be triply continuous.

Thomson showed that the proper modification of the theorem is obtained by imagining diaphragms placed across the space, which are not to be crossed by any closed path drawn within the space, and the two surfaces of each of which are to be reckoned as part of the bounding surface of the space. One such diaphragm is sufficient to convert a hollow anchor-ring into a singly continuous space, two would be required for the hollow anchor-ring with cross-connection, and so on. The number of diaphragms required is always one less than the degree of multiplicity of the continuity.

The paper also deals with the motion of solids in the fluid and the analogous motions of vortex-rings and their attraction by ordinary matter. These can be studied with vortex-rings in air produced by the apparatus described above. Such a ring made to pass the re-entrant corner of a wall—the edge of a window recess, for example—will appear to be attracted. A large sphere such as a large terrestrial globe serves also very well as an attracting body.

Two vortex-rings projected one after the other also

act on one another in a very curious manner. Their planes are perpendicular to the direction of motion, and the fluid is moving round the circular core of the ring. There is irrotational cyclic motion of the fluid through the ring in one direction and back outside, as shown in Fig. 13, which can be detected by placing a candle flame in the path of the centre. The first ring, in consequence of the existence of that which follows it, moves more slowly, and opens out more widely, the following ring hastens its motion and diminishes in diameter, until finally it overtakes the former and penetrates it. As soon as it has passed through it moves ahead more and more slowly, until the one which has been left behind begins to catch it up, and the changes which took place before are repeated. The one penetrating becomes in its turn the penetrated, and so on in alternation. Great care and skill are, however, necessary to make this interesting experiment succeed.

We have not space to deal here with other hydro-dynamical investigations, such as the contributions which Thomson made to the discussion of the many difficult problems of the motion of solids through a liquid, or to his very numerous and important contributions to the theory of waves. The number and importance of his hydrodynamical papers may be judged from the fact that there are no less than fifty-two references to his papers, and thirty-five to Thomson and Tait's *Natural Philosophy* in the latest edition of Lamb's *Hydrodynamics*, and that many of these are concerned with general theorems and results of great value.

CHAPTER X

Electrolysis and Electrical Units

In December 1851 Thomson communicated an important paper to the *Philosophical Magazine* on " The Mechanical Theory of Electrolysis," and " Applications of Mechanical Effect to the Measurement of Electromotive Forces, and of Galvanic Resistances, in Absolute Units."

In the first of these he supposed a machine of the kind imagined by Faraday, consisting of a metal disk, rotating uniformly with its plane at right angles to the lines of force of a uniform magnetic field, and touched at its centre and its circumference by fixed wires, to send a current through an electrochemical apparatus, to which the wires are connected. A certain amount of work W was supposed to be spent in a given time, during which a quantity of heat H was evolved in the circuit, and a certain amount of work M spent in the chemical apparatus in effecting chemical change. If H be taken in dynamical units, $W = H + M$.

The work done in driving the disk, if the intensity of the field is I, the current produced c, the radius of the disc r, and the angular velocity of turning w, is $\frac{1}{2}Ir^2cw$.

Thomson assumed that the work done in the electrochemical apparatus was equal to the heat of chemical combination of the substance or substances which underwent the chemical action, taken with the proper sign according to the change, if more compound substances than one were acted on. Hence M represented this resultant heat of combination.

The electrochemical apparatus was a voltameter containing a definite compound to be electrolysed, or a voltaic cell or battery. And by Faraday's experiments on electrolysis it was known that the amount of chemical action was proportional to the whole quantity of electricity passed through the cell in a given time, so that the rate at which energy was being spent in the cell was at any instant proportional to the current at that instant.

The chemical change could be measured by considering only one of the elements set free, or made to combine, by the passage of the current, and considering the quantity of heat θ, say, for the whole chemical change in the cell corresponding to the action on unit mass of that element. Thus if E denote the whole quantity of that element operated on the heat of combination in the vessel was θE. If E be taken for unit of time, and ϵ denote the quantity set free by the passage of unit quantity of electricity, then $E = \epsilon c$, since a current conveys c units of electricity in one second. The number ϵ is a definite quantity of the element, and is called its electrochemical equivalent. Again, from Joule's experiments, $H = Rc^2$, if R denote the resistance of the current, and so

$$\tfrac{1}{2}Ir^2cw = Rc^2 + \theta\epsilon c$$

and
$$c = \frac{\tfrac{1}{2}Ir^2w - \theta\epsilon}{R}$$

The quantity $\frac{1}{2}Ir^2w$ is the electromotive force due to the disk.

Thus c was positive or negative according as $\frac{1}{2}Ir^2w$ was greater or less than $\theta\epsilon$, and was zero when $\frac{1}{2}Ir^2w = \theta\epsilon$. Thus the electromotive force of the disk was opposed by a back electromotive force $\theta\epsilon$ due to the chemical action in the voltameter or battery, to which the wires from the disk were connected.

The conclusion arrived at therefore was that the electromotive force (or, as it was then termed, the intensity) of the electrochemical action was equal to the dynamical value of the whole chemical change effected by a current of unit strength in unit of time.

From this result Thomson proceeded to calculate the electromotive forces required to effect chemical changes of different kinds, and those of various types of voltaic cell. Supposing a unit of electricity to be carried by the current through the cell, he considered the chemical changes which accompanied its passage, and from the known values of heats of combination calculated their energy values. In some parts the change was one of chemical combination, in others one of decomposition of the materials, and regard had to be paid to the sign of the heat-equivalent. By properly summing up the whole heat-equivalents a net total was obtained which, according to Thomson, was the energy consumed in the passage of unit current, and was therefore the electromotive force. The theory was incomplete, and required to be supplemented by thermodynamic theory, which shows that besides the electromotive force there must be included in the quantity set against the sum of heats a term represented by the product of the absolute temperature multiplied by the rate of variation of electromotive force with alteration of temperature. Thus the theory is only applicable when the electromotive force is not affected by variation of temperature. The necessary addition here indicated was made by Helmholtz.

In the next paper, which appeared in the same number (December 1851) of the *Philosophical Magazine*, the principle of work is applied to the measurement of electromotive forces and resistances in absolute units. The advantages of such units are obvious. Nearly the whole of the quantitative work of the older experimenters was useless except for those who had actually made the observations : it was hardly possible for one man to advance his researches by employing data obtained by others. For the results were expressed by reference to apparatus and materials in the possession of the observers, and to these others could obtain access only with great difficulty and at great expense—to say nothing of the uncertainty of comparisons made to enable the results of one man to be linked on to those made elsewhere, and with other apparatus, by another. It was imperative, therefore, to obtain absolute units— units independent of accidents of place and apparatus— for the expression of currents, electromotive forces, and resistances, so as to enable the results of the work of experiments all over the world to be made available to every one who read the published record. (See Chap. XIII.)

The magneto-electric machine imagined in the former paper gave a means of estimating the electromotive force of a cell or battery in absolute units. The same kind of machine is used here, in the simpler form of a sliding conductor connecting a pair of insulated

rails laid with their plane perpendicular to the lines of
force of a uniform magnetic field. If the rails be
connected by a wire, and the slider be moved so as to
cut across the lines of force, a current will be produced
in the circuit. The current can be measured in terms
of the already known unit of current, that current
which flowing in a circle of radius unity produces a
magnetic field at the centre of 2π units. This current,
c, say, in strength, flowing in the circuit, renders a
dynamical force cIl necessary to move the slider of
length l across the lines of force of the field of intensity
I, and if the speed of the slider required for the current
c be v, the rate at which work is done in moving the
slider is $cIlv$. This must be the rate at which work is
done in the circuit by the current, and if the only
work done be in the heating of the conductor, we have
$cIlv = Rc^2$, or $Ilv = Rc$, so that Ilv is the electromotive force. Any electromotive force otherwise
produced, which gave rise to the same current, must
obviously be equal to Ilv, so that the unit of electromotive force can thus be properly defined.

Thomson used a foot-grain-second system of units;
but from this arrangement are now obtained the C.G.S.
units of electromotive force and resistance. If I is one
C.G.S. unit, l one centimetre, and v one centimetre
per second, we have unit electromotive force in the
C.G.S. system. Also in one C.G.S. unit of resistance
if c be unity as well as Ilv.

The idea of the determination of a resistance in
absolute units on correct principles was due to W.
Weber, who also gave methods of carrying out the
measurement; and the first determination was made
by Kirchhoff in 1849. Thomson appears, however,

to have been the first to discuss the subject of units from the point of view of energy. This mode of regarding the matter is important, as the absolute units are so chosen as to enable work done by electric and magnetic forces to be reckoned in the ordinary dynamical units. A vast amount of experimental resource and skill has been spent since that time on the determination of resistance, though not more than the importance of the subject warranted. We shall have to return to the subject in dealing with the work of the British Association on Electrical Standards, of which Thomson was for long an active member.

ELECTRICAL OSCILLATIONS

In his famous tract on the conservation of energy, published in 1847, von Helmholtz discussed some puzzling results obtained by Riess in the magnetisation of iron wires by the current of a Leyden jar discharge flowing in a coil surrounding them, and by the fact, observed by Wollaston, that when water was decomposed by Leyden jar discharges a mixture of oxygen and hydrogen appeared at each electrode, and suggested that possibly the discharge was oscillatory in character.

In 1853 the subject was discussed mathematically by Thomson, in a paper which was to prove fruitful in our own time in a manner then little anticipated. The jar is given, let us say, with the interior coating charged positively, and the exterior coating charged negatively. A coil or helix of wire has its ends connected to the two coatings, and a current immediately begins in the wire, and gradually (not slowly) increases in strength. Accompanying the creation of the current is the production of a magnetic field, that is, the surrounding space is made the seat of magnetic action. The magnetic field, as we shall see from another investigation of Thomson's, almost certainly involves motion in or of a medium—the ether—filling the space where the magnetic action is found to exist. The charge of the jar consists of a state of intense and peculiar strain in the glass plate between the coatings. When the plates are connected by the coil, this state of strain breaks down and motion in the medium ensues, not merely between the plates, but also in the surrounding space—in fact, in the whole field. This motion—which is not to be confused with bodily displacement of finite parts of the medium—is opposed by something akin to inertia of the medium (the property that confers energy on matter when in motion), so that when the motion is started it persists, until it is finally wiped out by resistance of the nature of friction. The inertia here referred to depends on the mode in which the coil is wound, or whether it contains or not an iron core.

If the work done in charging a Leyden jar or electric condenser, by bringing the charge to the condenser in successive small portions, is considered, it is at once clear that it must be proportional to the square of the whole quantity of electricity brought up. For whatever the charge may be, let it be brought up from a great distance in a large number N of equal instalments. The larger the whole amount the larger must each instalment be, and therefore the greater the amount accumulated on the condenser when any given number of instalments have been deposited. But the greater any charge that is being brought up, and also the greater the charge that has already arrived, the greater is the repulsion that must be overcome in bringing up that instalment, in simple proportion in each case, and therefore the greater the work done. Thus the whole work done in bringing up the charge must be proportional to Q^2. We suppose it to be $\frac{1}{2}Q^2/C$, where C is a constant depending on the condenser and called its capacity.

The idea of the charge as a quantity of some kind of matter, brought up and placed on the insulated plate of the condenser, has only a correspondence to the fact, which is that the medium between the plates is the seat, when the condenser is charged, of a store of energy, which can only be made available by connecting the plates of the condenser by a wire or other conductor. The charge is only a surface aspect of the state of the medium, apparently a state of strain, to which the energy belongs.

When a wire is used to connect the plates the state of strain disappears; the energy comes out from the medium between the plates by motion sideways of the tubes of strain (so that the insulating medium is under longitudinal tension and lateral pressure) which, according to Faraday's conception of lines of electric force connecting the charge on a body with the opposite charges on other bodies, run from plate to plate, when the condenser is in equilibrium in the changed state. These tubes move out with their ends on the wire, carrying the energy with them, and the ends run towards one another along the wire; the tube shortens in the process, and energy is lost in the wire. The ends of a tube thus moving represent portions of the charges which were on the plates, and the oppositely-directed motions of the opposite charges represent a current along the wire from one conductor to the other. The motion of the tubes is accompanied by the development of a magnetic field, the lines of force of which are endless, and the direction of which at every point is perpendicular at once to the length of the tube and to the direction in which it is there moving. In certain circumstances the tube, by the time its ends have met, will have wholly disappeared in the wire, and the whole energy will have gone to heat the wire : in other circumstances the ends will meet before the tube has disappeared, the ends will cross, and the tube will be carried back to the condenser and reinserted in the opposite direction. At a certain time this will have happened to all the tubes, though they will have lost some of their energy in the process ; and the condenser will again be charged, though in the opposite way to that in which it was at first. Then the tubes will move out again, and the same process will be repeated : once more the condenser will be charged, but in the same direction as at first, and once more with a certain loss of energy. Again the process of discharge and charge will take place, and so on, again and again, until the whole energy has disappeared. This process represents, according to the modern theory of the flow of energy in the electromagnetic field, with more or less accuracy, what takes place in the oscillatory discharge of a condenser.

The motion of the tubes with their ends on the wire represents a certain amount of energy, commonly regarded as kinetic, and styled electrokinetic energy. If c denote the current, that is, the rate, $-dQ/dt$, at which the charge of the condenser is being changed, and L a quantity called self-inductance, depending

mainly on the arrangement of the connecting wire—
whether it is wound in a coil or helix, with or without
an iron core, or not—the electrokinetic energy will be
$\frac{1}{2}Lc^2$. This is analogous to the kinetic energy $\frac{1}{2}mv^2$
of a body (say a pendulum bob) of mass m and velocity
v, so that L represents a quantity for the conducting
arrangement analogous to inertia, and c is the analogue
of the velocity of the body. The whole energy at
any instant is thus

$$\tfrac{1}{2}Q^2 / C + \tfrac{1}{2}Lc^2, \text{ or } \tfrac{1}{2}Q^2 / C + \tfrac{1}{2}L \, (dQ / dt)^2.$$

The loss of energy due to heating of the conducting
connection is not completely understood, though its
quantitative laws have been quite fully ascertained and
expressed in terms of magnitudes that are capable of
measurement. It was found by Joule to be proportional to the second power, or square, of the current,
and to a quantity R depending on the conductor, and
called its resistance. The generation of heat in the
conductor seems to be due to some kind of frictional
action of particles of the conductor set up by the pene-
tration of the Faraday tubes into it. A conductor is
unable to bear any tangential action exerted upon it by
Faraday tubes, which, however, when they exist, begin
and end at material particles, except when they are
endless, as they may be in the radiation of energy.
When the Faraday tubes are moving with any ordinary
speed they are not at their ends perpendicular to the
conducting surface from which they start or at which
they terminate, but are there more or less inclined to
the surface, and consequently there is tangential action
which appears to displace the particles (not merely
at the surface, unless the alternation is very rapid)

relatively to one another and so cause frictional generation of heat.

The time rate of generation of heat is thus Rc^2, or $R(dQ/dt)^2$, when the units in which R and c are expressed are such as to make this quantity a rate of doing work in the true dynamical sense. This is the rate at which the sum of energy already found is being diminished, and so the equation

$$\tfrac{1}{2}\frac{d}{dt}\left\{\frac{Q^2}{C} + L\left(\frac{dQ}{dt}\right)^2\right\} = -R\left(\frac{dQ}{dt}\right)^2$$

holds, or leaving out the common factor dQ/dt, the equation

$$L\frac{d^2Q}{dt^2} + R\frac{dQ}{dt} + \frac{Q}{C} = 0$$

This last equation was established by Thomson, and is precisely that which would be obtained for a pendulum bob of mass L, pulled back towards the position of equilibrium with a force Q/C, where Q is the displacement from the middle position, and having its motion damped out by resisting force of amount R per unit of the velocity.

It is more instructive perhaps to take the oscillatory motion of a spiral spring hung vertically with a weight on its lower end, as that which has a differential equation equivalent to the equation just found. When the stretch is of a certain amount, there is equilibrium —the action of the spring just balances the weight,— and if the spring be stretched further there will be a balance of pull developed tending to bring the system back towards the equilibrium position. If left to itself the system gets into motion, which, if the resistance is not too great, is added to until the equilibrium position is reached ; and the motion, which is continued by the inertia of the mass, only begins to fall off as that position is passed, and the pull of the spring becomes insufficient to balance the weight. Thus the mass oscillates about the position of equilibrium, and the oscillations are successively smaller and smaller in extent, and die out as their energy is expended finally in doing work against friction.

If the resisting force for finite motion is very great, as for example when the vibrating mass of the pendulum or spring is immersed in a very viscous fluid, like treacle, oscillation will not take place at all. After displacement the mass will move at first fairly quickly, then more and more slowly back to the position of equilibrium, which it will, strictly speaking, only exactly reach after an infinite time. The resisting force is here indefinitely small for an indefinitely small speed, but it becomes so great when any motion ensues, that as the restoring force falls off with the displacement, no work is finally done by it, except to move the body through the resisting medium.

The differential equation is applicable to the spring if Q is again taken as displacement from the equilibrium position, L as the inertia of the vibrating body, $1/C$ as the pull exerted by the spring per unit of its extension (that is, the stiffness of the spring), and R has the same meaning as before.

In this case of motion, as well as in that of the pendulum, energy is carried off by the production of waves in the medium in which the vibrator is immersed. These are propagated out from the vibrator as their source, but no account of them is taken in the differential equation, which in that respect is imperfect. There is no difficulty, only the addition of a little complication, in supplying the omission.

The formation of such waves by the spiral spring vibrator can be well shown by immersing the vibrating body in a trough of water, and the much greater rate of damping out of the motion in that case can then be compared with the rate of damping in air.

It has been indicated that the differential equation does not represent oscillatory motion if the value of R is too great. The exact condition depends on the roots of the quadratic equation $Lx^2 + Rx + 1/C = 0$, obtained by writing 1 for Q, and x for d/dt, and then treating x as a quantity. These roots are $-R/2L \pm \sqrt{R^2/4L^2 - 1/CL}$, and are therefore real or imaginary according as $4L/C$ is less or greater than R^2. If the roots are real, that is, if R^2 be greater than $4L/C$, the discharge will not be oscillatory ; the Faraday tubes referred to above will be absorbed in the wire without any return to the condenser. The corresponding result happens with the vibrator when R is sufficiently great, or L/C sufficiently small (a weak spring and a small mass, or both), to enable the condition to be fulfilled.

If, however, the roots of the quadratic are imaginary, that is, if $4L/C$ be greater than R^2 (a condition which will be fulfilled in the spring analogue, by making the spring sufficiently stiff and the mass large enough to prevent the friction from controlling the motion) the motion is one in which Q disappears by oscillations about zero, of continually diminishing amplitude. A complete discussion gives for the period of oscillation $4\pi L/\sqrt{4L/C - R^2}$, or if R be comparatively small,

$2\pi\sqrt{LC}$. The charge Q falls off by the fraction $e^{-RT/2L}$ (where e is the number 2·71828 . . .) in each period T, and so gradually disappears.

Thus electric oscillations are produced, that is to say, the charged state of the condenser subsides by oscillations, in which the charged state undergoes successive reversals, with dissipation of energy in the wire ; and both the period and the rate of dissipation can be calculated if L, C, and R are known, or can be found, for the system. These quantities can be calculated and adjusted in certain definite cases, and as the electric oscillations can be experimentally observed, the theory can be verified. This has been done by various experimenters.

Returning to the pendulum illustration, it will be seen that the pendulum held deflected is analogous to the charged jar, letting the pendulum go corresponds to connecting the discharging coil to the coatings, the motion of the pendulum is the analogue of that motion of the medium in which consists the magnetic field, the friction of the air answers to the resistance of the wire which finally damps out the current. The inertia or mass of the bob is the analogue of what Thomson called the electromagnetic inertia of the coil and connections ; what is now generally called the self-inductance of the conducting system. The component of gravity along the path towards the lowest point, answers to the reciprocal, $1 / C$, of the capacity of the condenser.

It appears from the analogy that just as the oscillations of a pendulum can be prevented by immersing the bob in a more resisting medium, such as treacle or oil, so that when released the pendulum slips down to the vertical without passing it, so by properly proportioning the resistance in the circuit to the electromagnetic inertia of the coil, oscillatory discharge of the Leyden jar may also be rendered impossible.

All this was worked out in an exceedingly instructive manner in Thomson's paper; the account of the matter by the motion of Faraday tubes is more recent, and is valuable as suggesting how the inertia effect of the coil arises. The analogy of the pendulum is a true one, and enables the facts to be described; but it is to be remembered that it becomes evident only as a consequence of the mathematical treatment of the electrical problem. The paper was of great importance for the investigation of the electric waves used in wireless telegraphy in our own time. It enabled the period of oscillation of different systems to be calculated, and so the rates of exciters and receivers of electric waves to be found. For such vibrators are really Leyden jars, or condensers, caused to discharge in an oscillatory manner.

This application was not foreseen by Thomson, and, indeed, could hardly be, as the idea of electric waves in an insulating medium came a good deal later in the work of Maxwell. Yet the analogy of the pendulum, if it had then been examined, might have suggested such waves. As the bob oscillates backwards and forwards the air in which it is immersed is periodically disturbed, and waves radiate outwards from it through the surrounding atmosphere. The energy of these waves is exceedingly small, otherwise, as pointed out above, a term would have to be included in the theory of the resisted motion of the pendulum to account for this energy of radiation. So likewise when the electric vibrations proceed, and the insulating medium is the seat of a periodically varying magnetic field, electromagnetic waves are propagated outwards through the surrounding medium—the ether—and the energy carried away by the waves is derived from the initial energy of the charged condenser. In strictness also Thomson's theory of electric oscillations requires an addition to account for the energy lost by radiation. This is wanting, and the whole decay of the amount of energy present at the oscillator is put down to the action of resistance—that is, to something of the nature of frictional retardation. Notwithstanding this defect of the theory, which is after all not so serious as certain difficulties of exact calculation of the self-inductance of the discharging conductor, the periods of vibrators can be very accurately found. When these are known it is only necessary to measure the length of an electrical wave to find its velocity of propagation. When electromagnetic waves were discovered experimentally in 1888 by Heinrich Hertz, it was thus that he was able to demonstrate that they travelled with the velocity of light.

Thomson suggested that double, triple and quadruple flashes of lightning might be successive flashes of an oscillatory discharge. He also pointed out that if a spark-gap were included in a properly arranged condenser and discharging wire, it might be possible, by means of Wheatstone's revolving mirror, to see the sparks produced in the successive oscillations, as " points or short lines of light separated by dark intervals, instead of a single point of light, or of an unbroken line of light, as it would be if the discharge were instantaneous, or were continuous, or of appreciable duration."

This anticipation was verified by experiments made by Feddersen, and published in 1859 (*Pogg. Ann.,* 108, 1859). The subject was also investigated in Helmholtz's laboratory at Berlin, by N. Schiller, who, determining the period for condensers with different substances between the plates, was able to deduce the inductive capacities of these substances (*Pogg. Ann.,* 152, 1874). [The specific inductive capacity of an insulator is the ratio of the capacity of a condenser with the substance between the plates to the capacity of an exactly similar condenser with air between the plates.]

The particular case of non-oscillatory discharge obtained by supposing C and Q both infinitely great and to have a finite ratio V (which will be the potential, p. 34, of the charged plate), is considered in the paper. The discharging conductor is thus subjected to a difference of potential suddenly applied and maintained at one end, while the other end is kept at potential zero. The solution of the differential equation for this case will show how the current rises from zero in the wire to its final steady value. If c be put as before for the current $- dQ/dt$, and the constant value V for Q/C, the equation is

$$L\frac{dc}{dt} + Rc = V$$

which gives, since $c = 0$ when $t = 0$,

$$c = \frac{V}{R}\left(1 - e^{-\frac{R}{L}t}\right).$$

Thus, when an infinite time has elapsed the current has become V/R, the steady value.

Thomson concludes by showing how, by measuring the non-oscillatory discharge of a condenser (the capacity of which can be calculated) by means of an electrodynamometer and an ordinary galvanometer arranged in series, what W. Weber called the duration of the discharging current may be determined. From this Thomson deduced a value for the ratio of the electromagnetic unit of electricity to the electrostatic unit, and indicated methods of determining this ratio experimentally. This ratio is of fundamental importance in electromagnetic theory, and is essentially of the nature of a speed. According to Maxwell it is the speed of propagation of electromagnetic waves in an insulating medium for which the units are defined. It was first determined in the Glasgow laboratory by Mr. Dugald McKichan, and has been determined many times since. It is practically identical with the speed of light as ascertained by the best experiments.

CHAPTER XI

THE 'NATURAL PHILOSOPHY'

PROFESSOR TAIT was appointed to the Chair of Natural Philosophy in the University of Edinburgh in 1860, and came almost immediately into frequent contact with Thomson. Both were Peterhouse men, trained by the same private tutor—William Hopkins—both were enthusiastic investigators in mathematical as well as in experimental physics, they taught in the sister universities of Edinburgh and Glasgow, and had much the same kind of classes to deal with and the same educational problems to solve. Tait was an Edinburgh man—an old school-fellow of Clerk Maxwell at the Edinburgh Academy—and had therefore been exposed to that contact, in play and in work, with compeers of like age and capabilities, which is one of the best preparations for the larger school and more serious struggles of life. Thomson's early education, under his father's anxious care, had no doubt certain advantages, and his early entrance into college classes gave him to a great extent that intercourse with others for which such advantages are never complete compensation. The two men had much

194

community of thought and experience, and the literary partnership into which they entered was hailed as one likely to do much for the progress of science.

In some ways, however, Thomson and Tait were very different personalities. Thomson troubled himself little with metaphysical subtleties, his conceptions were like those of Newton, absolutely clear so far as they went ; he never, in his teaching at least, showed any disposition to discuss the "foundations of dynamics," or the conception of motion in a straight line. These were taken for granted like the fundamental ideas in a book on geometry ; and the student was left to do what every true dynamical student must do for himself sooner or later—to compare the abstractions of dynamics with the products of his experience in the world of matter and force. Perhaps a little guidance now and then in the difficulties about conceptions, which beset every beginner, might not have been amiss : but Thomson was so intent on the concrete example in hand—pendulum or gyrostat, or what not —that he left each man to form or correct his own ideas by the lessons which such examples afford to every one who carefully examines them.

Tait, on the other hand, though he continually denounced metaphysical discussion, was in reality much more metaphysical than Thomson, and seemed to take pleasure in the somewhat transcendental arguments with regard to matters of analysis which were put forward, especially in the *Elements of Quaternions*, by Sir William Rowan Hamilton, of Dublin, a master whom he much revered. But there is metaphysics and metaphysics ! and the pronouncements of professed metaphysicians were often characterised as non-scientific and fruitless, which no doubt they were from the physical point of view.

Then Tait was strongly convinced of the importance for physics of the quaternion analysis: Thomson was not, to say the least; and this was probably the main reason why the vectorial treatment of displacement, velocities, and other directed quantities, has no place in the joint writings of the two Scottish professors. In controversy Tait was a formidable antagonist: when war was declared he gave no quarter and asked for none, though he never fought an unchivalric battle. He admired foreign investigators—and especially von Helmholtz—but he was always ready to put on his armour and place lance in rest for the cause of British science. Thomson was much less of a combatant, though he also could bravely splinter a spear with an opponent on occasion, as in the memorable discussion with Huxley on the Age of the Earth.

Tait's professorial lectures were always models of clear and logical arrangement. Every statement bore on the business in hand; the experimental illustrations, always carefully prepared beforehand, were called for at the proper time and were invariably successful. With Thomson it was otherwise: his digressions, though sometimes inspired and inspiring, were fatal to the success of the utmost efforts of his assistants to make his lectures successful systematic expositions of the facts and principles of elementary physics.

As has been stated in Chapter IV, two books were announced in 1863 as in course of preparation for the ensuing session of College. These were not published until 1867 and 1873; the first issued was the famous *Treatise on Natural Philosophy*, the second was entitled

Elements of Natural Philosophy, and consisted in the main of part of the non-mathematical or large type portions of the *Treatise*. The scheme of the latter was that of an articulated skeleton of statements of principles and results, printed in ordinary type, with the mathematical deductions and proofs in smaller type. As was to be expected, the *Elements*, to a student whose mathematical reading was wide enough to tackle the *Treatise*, was the more difficult book of the two to completely master. But the continued large print narrative, as it may be called, is extremely valuable. It is a memorial of a habit of mind which was characteristic of both authors. They kept before them always the idea or thing rather than its symbol ; and thus the edifice which they built up seemed never obscured by the scaffolding and machinery used in its erection. And as far as possible in processes of deduction the ideas are emphasised throughout ; there is no mere putting in at one end and taking out at the other ; the result is examined and described at every stage. As in all else of Thomson's work, physical interpretation is kept in view at every step, and made available for correction and avoidance of errors, and the suggestion of new inquiries.

The book as it stands consists of "Division I, Preliminary" and part of "Division II, Abstract Dynamics." Division I includes the chapter on Kinematics already referred to, a chapter on Dynamical Laws and Principles, chapters on Experience and Measures and Instruments. Division II is represented only by Chapter V, Introductory ; Chapter VI, Statics of a Particle and Attractions ; and Chapter VII, Statics of Solids and Fluids. Thus Abstract Dynamics is without the more complete treatment of Kinetics to which, as well as to Statics, the discussion of Dynamical Laws and Principles was intended to be an introduction. But to a considerable extent, as we shall see, Kinetics is treated in this introductory chapter : indeed, the discussion of the general theorems of dynamics and their applications to kinetics is remarkably complete.

In Volume II it was intended to include chapters on the kinetics of a particle and of solid and fluid bodies, on the vibrations of solid bodies, and on wave-motion in general. It was expected also to contain a chapter much referred to in Volume I, on "Properties of Matter." That the work was not completed is a matter of keen regret to all physicists, regret, however, now tempered by the fact that many of the subjects of the unfulfilled programme are represented by such works as Lord Rayleigh's *Theory of Sound*, Lamb's *Hydrodynamics*, and Routh's *Dynamics of a System of Rigid Bodies*. But all deeply lament the loss of the "Properties of Matter." No one can ever write it as Thomson would have written it. His students obtained in his lectures glimpses of the things it might have contained, and it was most eagerly looked for. If that chapter only had been given, the loss caused by the discontinuance of the book would not have been so irreparable.

The first edition of the book was published by the Clarendon Press, Oxford. It was printed by Messrs. Constable, of Edinburgh, and is a beautiful specimen of mathematical typography. In some ways the first edition is exceedingly interesting, for it is not too much to say that its issue had an influence on dynamical science, and its exposition in this country, only second to that due to Newton's *Principia*. Three other works, perhaps, have had the same degree and kind of influence on mathematical thought—Laplace's *Mécanique Céleste*, Lagrange's *Mécanique Analytique*, and Fourier's *Théorie Analytique de la Chaleur*.

The second edition was issued by the Cambridge University Press as Parts I and II in 1878 and 1883. Various younger mathematicians now of eminence— Professor Chrystal, of Edinburgh, and Professor Burnside, of Greenwich, may be mentioned—read the proofs, and it is on the whole remarkably free from typographical and other errors. With the issue of Part II, the continuation was definitely abandoned.

In the second edition many topics are more fully discussed, and the contents include a very valuable account of cycloidal motion (or oscillatory motion, as it is more usually called), and of a revised version of the chapter on Statics which forms the concluding portion of the book, and which discusses some of the great problems of terrestrial and cosmical physics.

Various speculations have been indulged in, from time to time, as to the respective parts contributed to the work by the two authors, but these are generally very wide of the mark. The mode of composition of the sections on cycloidal (oscillatory) motion gives some idea of Thomson's method of working. His proofs (of "T and T-*dash*" as the authors called the book) were carried with him by rail and steamer, and he worked incessantly (without, however, altogether withdrawing his attention from what was going on around him!) at corrections and additions. He corrected heavily on the proofs, and then overflowed into additional manuscript. Thus, when he came to the

short original § 343, he greatly extended that in the
first instance, and proceeded from section to section
until additions numbered from § 343*a* to § 343*p*,
amounting in all to some ten pages of small print,
had been interpolated.   Similarly § 345 was extended
by the addition of §§ 345 (i) to 345 (xxviii), mainly
on gyrostatic domination.   The method had the dis-
advantage of interrupting the printers and keeping type
long standing, but the matter was often all the more
inspiring through having been produced under pressure
from the printing office.   Indeed, much was no doubt
written in this way which, to the great loss of dynamical
science, would otherwise never have been written at all.

The kinematical discussion begins with the consideration of motion along a continuous line, curved
or straight.   This naturally suggests the ideas of
curvature and tortuosity, which are fully dealt with
mathematically, before the notion of velocity is introduced.   When that is done, the directional quality of
velocity is not so much insisted on as is now the case :
for example, a point is spoken of as moving in a
curve with a uniform velocity ; and of course in the
language of the present time, which has been rendered
more precise by vector ideas, if not by vector-analysis,
the velocity of a point which is continually changing
the direction of its motion, cannot be uniform.   The
same remark may be made regarding the treatment of
acceleration : in both cases the reference of the quantity
to three Cartesian axes is immediate, and the changes
of the components, thus fixed in direction, are alone
considered.

There can be no doubt that greater clearness is
obtained by the process afterwards insisted on by Tait,

of considering by a hodographic diagram the changes of velocity in successive intervals of time, and from these discovering the direction and magnitude of the rate of change at each instant. This method is indeed indicated at § 37, but no diagram is given, and the properties of the hodograph are investigated by means of Cartesians. The subject is, however, treated in the *Elements* by the method here indicated.

Remarkable features of this chapter are the very complete discussion of simple harmonic or vibratory motion, the sections on rotation, and the geometry of rolling and precessional motion, and on the curvature of surfaces as investigated by kinematical methods. A remark made in § 96 should be borne in mind by all who essay to solve gyrostatic problems. It is that just as acceleration, which is always at right angles to the motion of a point, produces a change in the direction of the motion but none in the *speed* of the point (it does influence the *velocity*), so an action, tending always to produce rotation about an axis at right angles to that about which a rigid body is already rotating, will change the direction of the axis about which the body revolves, but will produce no change in the rate of turning.[1]

[1] To this may be added the extremely useful theorem for such problems, that if any directed quantity L, say, characteristic of the motion of a body, be associated with a line or axis Ol, which is changing in direction, it causes a rate of production of the same quantity for a line or axis instantaneously at right angles to Ol, towards which Ol is turning with angular velocity ω, of amount ωL. If M be the amount of the quantity already existing for this latter line or axis, the total rate of growth of the quantity is there $\dot{M} + \omega L$. For example, a particle moving with uniform speed v in a circle of radius r, has momentum mv along the tangent. But the tangent is turning round as the particle moves with angular speed v / r, towards the radius. The rate of growth of momentum towards the centre is therefore

$$mv \times v / r = mv^2 / r.$$

A very full and clear account of the analysis of
strains is given in this chapter, in preparation for the
treatment of elasticity which comes later in the book ;
and a long appendix is added on Spherical Harmonics,
which are defined as homogeneous functions of the
coordinates which satisfy the differential equation of
the distribution of temperature in a medium in which
there is steady flow of heat, or of distribution of
potential in an electrical field. This appendix is
within its scope one of the most masterly discussions
of this subject ever written, though, from the point
of view of rigidity of proof, required by modern
function-theory, it may be open to objection.

In the next chapter, which is entitled " Dynamical
Laws and Principles," the authors at the outset declare
their intention of following the *Principia* closely in the
discussion of the general foundations of the subject.
Accordingly, after some definitions the laws of motion
are stated, and the opportunity is taken to adopt and
enforce the Gaussian system of absolute units for
dynamical quantities. As has been indicated above,
the various difficulties more or less metaphysical which
must occur to every thoughtful student in considering
Newton's laws of motion are not discussed, and probably
such a discussion was beyond the scheme which the
authors had in view. But metaphysics is not altogether
excluded. It is stated that " matter has an innate
power of resisting external influences, so that every
body, as far as it can, remains at rest, or moves
uniformly in a straight line," and it is stated that this
property—inertia—is proportional to the quantity of
matter in the body. This statement is criticised by
Maxwell in his review of the *Natural Philosophy* in

Nature in 1879 (one of the last papers that Maxwell wrote). He asks, "Is it a fact that 'matter has any power, either innate or acquired, of resisting external influences'? Does not every force which acts on a body always produce that change in the motion of the body by which its value, as a force, is reckoned? Is a cup of tea to be accused of resisting the sweetening influence of sugar, because it persistently refuses to turn sweet unless the sugar is put into it?"

This innate power of resisting is merely the *materiæ vis insita* of Newton's "Definitio III," given in the *Principia*, and the statement to which Maxwell objects is only a free translation of that definition. Moreover, when a body is drawn or pushed by other bodies, it reacts on those bodies with an equal force, and this reaction is just as real as the action : its existence is due to the inertia of the body. The definition, from one point of view, is only a statement of the fact that the acceleration produced in a body in certain circumstances depends upon the body itself, as well as on the other bodies concerned, but from another it may be regarded as accounting for the reaction. The mass or inertia of the body is only such a number that, for different bodies in the same circumstances as to the action of other bodies in giving them acceleration, the product of the mass and the acceleration is the same for all. It is, however, a very important property of the body, for it is one factor of the quantum of kinetic energy which the body contributes to the energy of the system, in consequence of its motion relatively to the chosen axes of reference, which are taken as at rest.

The relativity of motion is not emphasised so greatly

in the *Natural Philosophy* as in some more modern treatises, but it is not overlooked ; and whatever may be the view taken as to the importance of dwelling on such considerations in a treatise on dynamics, there can be no doubt that the return to Newton was on the whole a salutary change of the manner of teaching the subject.

The treatment of force in the first and second laws of motion is frankly causal. Force is there the *cause* of rate of change of momentum ; and this view Professor Tait in his own writings has always combated, it must be admitted, in a very cogent manner. According to him, force is merely rate of change of momentum. Hence the forces in equations of motion are only expressions, the values of which as rates of change of momentum, are to be made explicit by the solution of such equations in terms of known quantities. And there does not seem to be any logical escape from this conclusion, though, except as a way of speaking, the reference to cause disappears.

The discussion of the third law of motion is particularly valuable, for, as is well known, attention was therein called to the fact that in the last sentences of the *Scholium* which Newton appended to his remarks on the third law, the rates of working of the acting and reacting forces between the bodies are equal and opposite. Thus the whole work done in any time by the parts of a system on one another is zero, and the doctrine of conservation of energy is virtually contained in Newton's statement. The only point in which the theory was not complete so far as ordinary dynamical actions are concerned, was in regard to work done against friction, for which, when heat was left out of account, there was no visible equivalent. Newton's statement of the equality of what Thomson and Tait called "activity" and "counter-activity" is, however, perfectly absolute. In the completion of the theory of energy on the side of the conversion of heat into work, Thomson, as we have seen, took a very prominent part.

After the introduction of the dynamical laws the most interesting part of this chapter is the elaborate discussion which it contains of the Lagrangian equations of motion, of the principle of Least Action, with the large number of extremely important applications of these theories. The originality and suggestiveness of this part of the book, taken alone, would entitle it to rank with the great classics—the *Mécanique Céleste*, the *Mécanique Analytique*, and the memoirs of Jacobi and Hamilton—all of which were an outcome of the *Principia*, and from which, with the *Principia*, the authors of the *Natural Philosophy* drew their inspiration.

It is perhaps the case, as Professor Tait himself suggested, that no one has yet arisen who can bend to the fullest extent the bow which Hamilton fashioned ; but when this Ulysses appears it will be found that his strength and skill have been nurtured by the study of the *Natural Philosophy*. Lagrange's equations are now, thanks to the physical reality which the expositions and examples of Thomson and Tait have given to generalised forces, coordinates, and velocities, applied to all kinds of systems which formerly seemed to be outside the range of dynamical treatment. As Maxwell put it, "The credit of breaking up the monopoly of the great masters of the spell, and making all their charms familiar in our ears as household words, belongs

in great measure to Thomson and Tait. The two
northern wizards were the first who, without com-
punction or dread, uttered in their mother tongue the
true and proper names of those dynamical concepts,
which the magicians of old were wont to invoke only
by the aid of muttered symbols and inarticulate equations. And now the feeblest among us can repeat the
words of power, and take part in dynamical discussions
which a few years ago we should have left to our
betters."

A very remarkable feature in this discussion is the
use made of the idea of "ignoration of coordinates."
The variables made use of in the Lagrangian equations
must be such as to enable the positions of the parts of
the system which determine the motion to be expressed
for any instant of time. These parts, by their displacements, control those of the other parts, through
the connections of the system. They are called the
independent coordinates, and sometimes the "degrees
of freedom," of the system. Into the expressions of the
kinetic and potential energies, from which by a formal
process the equations of motion, as many in number
as there are degrees of freedom, are derived, the value
of these variables and of the corresponding velocities
enter in the general case. But in certain cases some
of the variables are represented by the corresponding
velocities only, and the variables themselves do not
appear in the equations of motion. For example, when
fly-wheels form part of the system, and are connected with the rest of the system only by their
bearings, the angle through which the wheel has
turned from any epoch of time is of no consequence,
the only thing which affects the energy of the system

is the angular velocity or angular momentum of the wheel. The system is said by Thomson and Tait in such a case to be under gyrostatic domination. (See "Gyrostatic Action," p. 214 below.)

Moreover, since the force which is the rate of growth of the momentum corresponding to any co-ordinate is numerically the rate of variation with that coordinate of the difference of the kinetic and potential energies, every force is zero for which the coordinate does not appear ; and therefore the corresponding momentum is constant. But that momentum is expressed by means of the values of other coordinates which do appear and their velocities, with the velocities for the absent coordinates ; and as many equations are furnished by the constant values of such momenta as there are coordinates absent. The corresponding velocities can be determined from these equations in terms of the constant momenta and the coordinates which appear and their velocities. The values so found, substituted in the expressions for the kinetic and potential energies, remove from these expressions every reference to the absent coordinates. Then from the new expression for the kinetic energy (in which a function of the constant momenta now appears, and is taken as an addition to the potential energy) the equations of motion are formed for the coordinates actually present, and these are sufficient to determine the motion. The other coordinates are thus in a certain sense ignored, and the method is called that of "ignoration of coordinates."

Theorems of action of great importance for a general theory of optics conclude this chapter ; but of these it is impossible to give here any account, without a discussion of technicalities beyond the reading of ordinary students of dynamics.

In an Appendix to Part I an account is given of Continuous Calculating Machines. Ordinary calculating machines, such as the " arithmometer " of Thomas of Colmar, carry out calculations and exhibit the result as a row of figures. But the machines here described are of a different character : they exhibit their results by values of a continuously varying quantity. The first is one for predicting the height of the tides for future time, at any port for which data have been already obtained regarding tidal heights, by means of a self-registering tide-gauge. Two of these were made according to the ideas set forth in this Appendix; one is in the South Kensington Museum, the other is at the National Physical Laboratory at Bushy House, where it is used mainly for drawing on paper curves of future tidal heights, for ports in the Indian Ocean. From these curves tide-tables are compiled, and issued for the use of mariners and others.

Another machine described in this Appendix was designed for the mechanical solution of simultaneous linear equations. It is impossible to explain here the interesting arrangement of six frames, carrying as many pulleys, adjustable along slides (for the solution of equations involving six unknown quantities), which Thomson constructed, and which is now in the Natural Philosophy Department at Glasgow. The idea of arranging the first practical machine for this number of variables, was that it might be used for the calculation of the corrections on values already found for the six elements of a comet or asteroid. The machine was made, but some mechanical difficulties arose in applying it, and the experiments with it were not at the time persevered with. Very possibly, however, it may yet be brought into use.

But the most wonderful of these mechanical arrangements is the machine for analysing the curves drawn by a self-registering tide gauge, so as to exhibit the constants of the harmonic curves, and thus enable the prediction of tidal heights to be carried out either by the tide-predicting machine, or by calculation. One day in 1876, Thomson remarked to his brother, James Thomson, then Professor of Engineering at

FIG. 14.

Glasgow, that all he required for the construction of a tidal analyser was a form of integrating machine more satisfactory for his purpose than the usual type of intregator employed by surveyors and naval architects. James Thomson at once replied that he had invented, a long time before, what he called a disk-globe-cylinder-integrator. This consisted of a brass disk, with its plane inclined to the horizontal, which could be turned about its axis by a wheel gearing in teeth on the edge of the disk, and driven by the operator in a manner which will presently appear. Parallel and close to the disk, but not touching it, was placed a horizontal cylinder

of brass, about 2 inches in diameter (called the registering cylinder), and between the disk and this cylinder
was laid a metal ball about $2\frac{1}{2}$ inches in diameter.
When the disk was kept at rest, and the ball was
rolled along between the cylinder and disk, the trace
of its rolling on the latter was a straight horizontal
line passing through the centre. Supposing then that the
point of contact of the ball with the disk was on one
side, at a distance from the centre, and that the disk
was then turned, the ball was by the friction between
it and the disk made to roll, and so to turn the
cylinder. The angular velocity of rolling, and therefore the angular velocity of the cylinder, was proportional to the speed of the part of the disk in contact
with it, that is, to y. It was also proportional to
the speed of turning of the disk.

The mode by which this machine effects an integration will now be evident. Imagine the area to be found
to lie between a curve and a straight datum line, drawn
on a band of paper. This is stretched on a large cylinder,
with the datum line round the cylinder. We call this
the paper-cylinder. The distances of the different points
of the curve from the datum line are values of y. A horizontal bar parallel to the cylinder carries a fork at one end
and a projecting style at the other. The globe just
fits between the prongs of the fork, and when the bar
is moved in the direction of its length carries the ball
along the disk and cylinder. When the style at the
other end is on the datum line, the centre of the ball
is at the centre of the disk, and the turning of the disk
does not turn the cylinder. When the bar is displaced
in the line of its own length to bring the style from the
datum line to a point on the curve, the ball is displaced

a distance y, and there is a corresponding turning of the
cylinder by the action of the ball. In the use of the
instrument the paper-cylinder is turned by the operator
while the style is kept on the curve, and the disk is
turned by the gearing already referred to, which is
driven by a shaft geared with that of the paper-cylinder.
Thus the displacement of the ball is always y, the
ordinate of the curve, and for any displacement dx
along the datum line, the registering cylinder is turned
through an angle proportional to ydx. Thus any finite
angle turned through is proportional to the integral of
ydx for the corresponding part of the curve : a scale
round one end of the registering cylinder gives that
angle. Thomson immediately perceived that this
extremely ingenious integrating machine was just
what he required for his purpose. The curve of
tidal heights drawn (on a reduced scale, of course) by a
tide-gauge, is really the resultant of a large number of
simple curves, represented by a series of harmonic
terms, the coefficients of which are certain integrals.
The problem is the evaluation of these integrals; and
the method usually employed is to obtain them by
measurement of ordinates of the curve and an elaborate
process of calculation. But one of them is simply the
integral area between the curve and the datum line
corresponding to the mean water level, and the others
are the integrals of quantities of the type $y \sin nx \cdot dx$,
where y is the ordinate of the curve, and n a number
inversely proportional to the period of the tidal con-
stituent represented by the term.

All that was necessary, in order to give the integral
of a term $y \sin nx \cdot dx$, was to make the disk oscillate
about its axis as the paper-cylinder was turned through

an angle proportional to x. Thus one disk, globe, and cylinder was arranged exactly as has been described for the integral of ydx, and with this as many others as there were harmonic terms to be evaluated from the curve were combined as follows. The disks were placed all in one plane with their centres all on one horizontal line, and the cylinders with their axes also in line, and a single sliding bar, with a fork for each globe, gave in each case the displacement y from the centre of the disk.

The requisite different speeds of oscillation were given to the disks by shafts geared with the paper-cylinder, by trains of wheels cut with the proper number of teeth for the speed required.

Thus the angles turned through by the registering cylinders when a curve on the paper-cylinder was passed under the style were proportional to the integrals required, and it was only necessary to calibrate the graduation of the scales of these cylinders by means of known curves to obtain the integrals in proper units.

One of these machines, which analyses four harmonic constituents, is in the Natural Philosophy Department at Glasgow ; a much larger machine, to analyse a tidal curve containing five pairs of harmonic terms, or eleven constituents in all, was made for the British Association Committee on Tidal Observations, and is probably now in the South Kensington Museum.

But still more remarkable applications which Thomson made of his brother's integrating machine were to the mechanical integration of linear differential equations, with variable coefficients, to the integration of the general linear differential equation of any order, and, finally, to the integration of any differential equation of any order.

These applications were all made in a few days, almost in a few hours, after James Thomson first described the elementary machine, and papers containing descriptions of the combinations required were at once dictated by Thomson to his secretary, and despatched for publication. Very possibly he had thought out the applications to some extent before ; but it is unlikely that he had done so in detail. But, even if it were so, the connection of a series of machines by the single controlling bar, and the production of the oscillations of the disks, all controlled, as they were, by the motion of a simple point along the curve, so as to give the required Fourier coefficients, were almost instantaneous, and afford an example of invention amounting to inspiration.

There should be noticed here also the geometrical slide for use in safety-valves, cathetometers and other instruments, and the hole-slot-and-plane mode of so supporting an instrument now used in all laboratories. These were Thomson's inventions, and their importance is insisted on in the *Natural Philosophy*.

In Part II, the principal subjects treated are attractions, elasticity, such great hydrostatical examples as the equilibrium theory of the tides and the equilibrium of rotating liquid spheroids, and such problems of astronomical and terrestrial dynamics as the distribution of matter in the earth, with the bearing on this subject of the precession of the equinoxes, tidal friction, the earth's rigidity, the effects of elastic tides, the secular cooling of the earth, the age of the earth, and

the "age of the sun's heat." Of these, with the exception of the age of the earth, we shall not attempt to
give any account. The importance of the original
contributions to elasticity contained in the book is
indicated by the large space devoted to the *Natural
Philosophy* in Professor Karl Pearson's continuation of
Todhunter's *History of Elasticity*. The heavy task of
editing Part II was performed mainly by Sir George
Darwin, who made many notable additions from his
own researches to the matter contained in the first
edition.

In the next chapter an attempt will be made to
present Thomson's views on the subject of the age
of the earth. These, when they were published,
attracted much attention, and received a good deal of
hostile criticism from geologists and biologists, whose
processes they were deemed to restrict to an entirely
inadequate period of time.

GYROSTATIC ACTION

Thomson in his lectures and otherwise gave a great
deal of attention to the motion of gyrostats, and to the
effect of the inclusion of gyrostats in a system on its
properties. Reference has been made to the treatment
of "gyrostatic domination" in "Thomson and Tait."
A gyrostat consists of a disk or wheel with a massive
rim, which revolves within a case or framework, by
which the whole arrangement can be moved about, or
supported, without interfering with the wheel. The
ordinary toy consisting of wheel with a massive rim, and
a light frame, is an example. But much larger and
more carefully made instruments, in which the wheel

is entirely enclosed, give the most interesting experiments. The body seems to have its properties entirely altered by the rotation of the wheel, and of course the case prevents any outward change from being visible.

Figure 15 shows one form of gyrostat mounted on a horizontal frame, held in the hands of an experimenter. The axis of the fly-wheel is vertical within the tubular part of the case; the fly-wheel is within the part on which is engraved an arrow-head to show the direction of rotation. Round the case in the

FIG. 15.

plane of the wheel is a projecting rim sharpened to an edge, on which the gyrostat can be supported in other experiments. To the rim are screwed two projecting pivots, which can turn in bearings on the two sides of the frame as shown. The centre of mass of the wheel is on the level of these pivots, so that the instrument will remain with either end of the axis up.

If the fly-wheel be not in rotation, the experimenter can carry the arrangement about, and the fly-wheel and case move with it as if the gyrostat were merely an ordinary rigid body. But now remove the gyrostat from the frame, and set the wheel in rotation. This is done by an endless cord wrapped round a small pulley fast on the axle (to which access is obtained by a hole just opposite in the case) and passed also round a larger pulley on the shaft of a motor. When the motor is started the cord must be tightened only very gently at first, so that it slips on the pulley, otherwise the motor would be retarded, and possibly burned by the current. The fly-wheel gradually gets up speed, and then the cord can be brought quite tight so that no slipping occurs. When the speed is great enough the cord is cut with a stroke from a sharp knife and runs out.

The gyrostat is now replaced on its pivots in the frame, with its axis vertical, and moved about as it was before. If the experimenter, holding the frame as shown, turns round in the direction of the arrow, which is that of rotation, nothing happens. If, however, he turns round the other way, the gyrostat immediately turns on its pivots so as to point the other end of the axis up. If the experimenter continues his turning motion, the gyrostat is now quiescent: for it is being carried round now in the direction of rotation. Thus, with no gravitational stability at all (since the centre is on a level with the pivots) the gyrostat is in stable equilibrium when carried round in the direction of rotation, but is in unstable equilibrium when carried round the opposite way.

Thus, if the observer knew nothing of the rotation of the fly-wheel, and could see and feel only the outside of the case, the behaviour of the instrument might well appear very astonishing.

This is a case of what Thomson and Tait call "gyrostatic domination," which is treated very fully in their Sections 345 (vi) to 345 (xxviii) of Part I. It may be remarked here that this case of motion may be easily treated mathematically in an exceedingly elementary manner, and the instability of the one case, and the stability of the other, made clear to the beginner who has only a notion of the composition of angular momenta about different axes.

A year or two ago it was suggested by Professor Pickering, of Harvard, that the fact that the outermost satellite of Saturn revolves in the direction opposite to the planet's rotation, may be due to the fact that originally Saturn rotated in the direction of the motion of this moon, but inasmuch as his motion round the sun was opposite in direction to his rotation, he was turned, so to speak, upside down, like the gyrostat ! The other satellites, it is suggested, were thrown off later, as their revolution is direct. Professor Pickering refers to an experiment (similar to that described above) which he gives as new. Thomson had shown this experiment for many years, as an example of the general discussion in "Thomson and Tait," and its theory had already been explicitly published.[1]

Many other experiments with gyrostats used to be shown by Thomson to visitors. Many of these are indicated in "Thomson and Tait." The earth's precessional motion is a gyrostatic effect due to the differential attraction of the sun, which tends to bring the plane of the equator into coincidence with the ecliptic, and so alters the direction of the axis of rotation. Old students will remember the balanced

[1] See Gray's *Lehrbuch der Physik*, s. 278. Vieweg u. Sohn, 1904.

globe—with inclined material axis rolling round a
horizontal ring—by which the kinematics of the
motion could be studied, and the displacement of the
equinoxes on the ecliptic traced.

Another example of the gyrostatic domination discussed in "Thomson and Tait" is given in the very
remarkable address entitled "A Kinetic Theory of

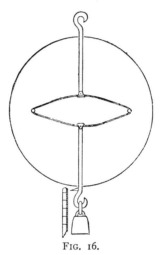

FIG. 16.

Matter," which Sir William Thomson delivered to
Section A of the British Association at Montreal, in
1884. Figure 16 shows an ordinary double "coach
spring," the upper and lower members of which
carry two hooked rods as shown. If the upper hook
is attached to a fixed support, and a weight is hung
on the lower, the spring will be drawn out, and the
arrangement will be in equilibrium under a certain
elongation. If the weight be pulled down further

and then left to itself, it will vibrate up and down
in a period depending upon the equilibrium elongation
produced by the weight. The same thing will happen
if a spiral spring be substituted for the coach spring.
A spherical case, through which the hooked rods pass
freely, hides the internal parts from view.

Figure 17 shows two hooked rods, as in the former
case, attached by swivels to two opposite corners of

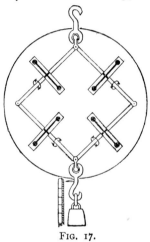

FIG. 17.

a frame formed of four rods jointed together at their
ends. Each of these is divided in the middle for the
insertion of a gyrostat, the axis of which is pivoted
on the adjacent ends of the two halves of the rod.
A spherical case, indicated by the circle, again hides
the internal arrangement from inspection, but permits
the hooked rods to move freely up and down. The
swivels allow the frame, gyrostats and all, to be turned
about the line of the hooks.

If now the gyrostats be not in rotation, the frame
will be perfectly limp, and will not in the least resist
pull applied by a weight. But if the gyrostats be rotated
in the directions shown by the circles, with arrow-
heads drawn round the rods, there will be angular
momentum of the whole system about the line joining
the hooks, and if a weight or a force be applied to
pull out the frame along that line, the pull will be
resisted just as it was in the other case by the spring.
Moreover, equilibrium will be obtained with an
elongation proportional to the weight hung on, and
small oscillations will be performed just as if there
were a spring in the interior instead of the gyrostats.

According as the frame is pulled out, or shortened,
the angular momentum of the gyrostats about the line
joining the hooks is increased or diminished, and the
frame, carrying the gyrostats with it, turns about
the swivels in one direction or the other, at the rate
necessary to maintain the angular momentum at a
constant value. But this will not be perceived from
without.

The rotation of the fly-wheels thus gives to the otherwise limp frame the elasticity which the spring possesses;
without dissection of the model the difference cannot
be perceived. This illustrates Thomson's idea that the
elasticity of matter may be due to motion of molecules
or groups of molecules of the body, imbedded in a
connecting framework, deformed by applied forces as
in this model, and producing displacements which are
resisted in consequence of the motion.

And here may be mentioned also Thomson's explanation of the phenomenon, discovered by Faraday,
of the rotation of the plane of a beam of polarised light

which is passed along the lines of force of a magnetic field. This rotation is distinct altogether from that which is produced when polarised light is passed along a tube filled with a solution of sugar or tartaric acid. If the ray be reflected after passage, and made to retraverse the medium, the rotation is annulled in the latter case, it is doubled in the former. This led Thomson to the view that in sugar, tartaric acid, quartz, etc., the turning is due to the structure of the substance, and in the magnetic field to rotation already existing in the medium. He used to say that a very large number of minute spiral cavities all in the same direction, and all right-handed or all left-handed, in the sugar or quartz, would give the effect ; on the other hand, the magnetic phenomenon could only be produced by some arrangement analogous to a very large number of tops, or gyrostats, imbedded in the medium with their axes all in one direction (or preponderatingly so) and all turning the same way. The rotation of these tops or gyrostats Thomson supposed to be caused by the magnetic field, and to be essentially that which constitutes the magnetisation of the medium.

Let the frame of the gyrostatic spring-balance described above, turn round the line joining the hooks so as to exactly compensate, by turning in the opposite direction, the angular momentum about that line given by the fly-wheels ; then the arrangement will have no angular momentum on the whole ; and a large number of such balances, all very minute and hooked together, will form a substance without angular momentum in any part. But now by the equivalent of a magnetic force along the lines of the hooks, let a different angular turning of the frames be produced ; the medium will possess a specific angular momentum in every part. If a wave of transverse vibrations which are parallel to one direction (that is, if the wave be plane-polarised) enter the medium in the direction of the axes of the frames, the direction of vibration will be turned as the wave proceeds, that is, the plane of polarisation will be turned round.

More recent research has shown an effect of a magnetic field on the spectrum of light produced in the field, and viewed with a spectroscope in a direction at right angles to the field—the Zeeman effect, as it is called—and the explanation of this effect by equations of moving electric charges, which are essentially gyrostatic equations, is suggestive of an analogy or correspondence between the systems of moving electrons which constitute these charges, and some such gyrostatic molecules as Thomson imagined. It has been pointed out that the Zeeman effect, in its simple forms at least, can be exactly imitated by the motion of an ordinary pendulum having a gyrostat in its bob, with its axis directed along the suspension rod.[1]

ELECTROSTATICS AND MAGNETISM

In the ten years from 1863 to 1873 Thomson was extremely busy with literary work. In 1872, five years after the publication of the treatise on *Natural Philosophy*, and just before the appearance of the *Elements*, Messrs. Macmillan & Co. published for him a collection of memoirs entitled *Reprint of Papers on*

[1] Gray, Royal Institution, Friday Evening Discourse, February 1898.

Electrostatics and Magnetism. The volume contains 596 pages, and the subjects dealt with range from the " Uniform Motion of Heat and its Connection with the Mathematical Theory of Electricity " (the paper already described in Chapter II above) and the discussion of Electrometers and Electrostatic Measuring Instruments, to a complete mathematical theory of magnetism. The subject of electrostatics led naturally to the consideration of electrical measuring instruments as they existed forty years ago (about 1867), and their replacement by others, the indications of which from day to day should be directly comparable, and capable of being interpreted in absolute units. Down to that time people had been obliged to content themselves with gold-leaf electroscopes, and indeed it was impossible for accurate *measuring* instruments to be invented until a system of absolute units had been completely worked out. The task of fixing upon definitions of units and of realising them in suitable standards had been begun by the British Association, and it was as part of the Report of that Committee to the Dundee Meeting in 1867 that Thomson's paper on Electrometers first appeared.

It was there pointed out that an electrometer is essentially an instrument for measuring differences of electric potential between conductors, by means of effects of electrostatic force. Such a difference is what a gold-leaf electroscope indicates for its gold leaves and the walls surrounding the air-space in which they are suspended. As electroscopes used to be constructed, these walls were made of glass imperfectly covered, if at all, by conducting material, and the electroscope was quite indefinite and uncertain in its action. The instrument was also, as made, quite insensitive. Recently, however, it has been rehabilitated in reputation, and brought into use as a very sensitive indicator of effects of radio-activity.

Thomson described in this paper six species of electrometers of his own devising. The best known of these are his quadrant electrometer and his attracted-disk electrometers. The former is to be found in some form or other in every laboratory nowadays, and need not be described in detail. The action is of two conductors—the two pairs of opposite quadrants of a shallow, horizontal, cylindrical box, made by dividing the box into four by two slits at right angles—upon an electrified slip of aluminium suspended by a two-thread suspension within the box, with its length along one of the slits. The two pairs of opposite quadrants are at the potential difference to be measured, and the slip of aluminium, or "needle," has each end urged round from a quadrant at higher potential towards one at a lower, and these actions conspire to turn the slip against its tendency to return to the position in which the two threads are in one plane. Thus the deflection (measured by the displacement of a reflected ray of light used as index) gives an indication of the amount of the potential difference.

The electrification of the "needle" was kept up by enclosing the quadrantal box within an electrified Leyden jar, to the interior coating of which contact is made by a platinum wire, depending from the needle to sulphuric acid contained in the jar. The whole apparatus was enclosed in a conducting case connected to earth. This made its action perfectly definite. Variations of this electrification of the jar were shown by an attached attracted-disk electrometer, the principle of which we shall merely indicate.

The quadrant electrometer has now been vastly increased in sensibility by the use of a single quartz fibre as suspension. By the invention of this fibre, which is exceedingly strong and is, moreover, so definite in its elastic properties that it comes back at once exactly to its former zero state after twist, Mr. C. V. Boys has increased the delicacy of all kinds of suspended indicators many fold. But it ought to be remembered that a Dolezalek electrometer, with some hundred or more times the sensibility of the bifilar instrument, was only made possible by its predecessor.

Attracted-disk-electrometers simply measure, either by weighing or by the deflection of a spring, the attractive force between two parallel disks at different potentials. From the determination of this force, and the measurement of the distance between the disks (or better, of an alteration of the distance) a difference of potentials can be determined, and a unit for it obtained, which is in direct and known relation to ordinary dynamical units. Thomson's "Absolute Electrometer" was designed specially for accurate determinations of this kind. Another form, called the Long Range Electrometer, was devised for the measurement of the potentials of the charged conductors in electric machines and Leyden jars.

Accurate determinations of the sparking resistance between parallel plates charged to different potentials in air were made by means of attracted-disk-electrometers in the course of some important experiments described in the *Electrostatics and Magnetism*. These results have been much referred to in later researches.

A small attracted-disk-electrometer was used as indicated above to keep a watch on the electrification of the Leyden jar of the quadrant instrument, and a small induction machine was added, by turning which the operator could make good any loss of charge of the jar.

This electrical machine was an example of an apparatus on precisely the same principle as the Voss or Wimshurst machines of the present day. In it by a set of moving carriers, influenced by conductors, the charges of the latter were increased according to a compound interest principle only interfered with by leakage to the air or by the supports. Several forms of this machine, on the same principle, were constructed by Thomson, and described in 1868 ; but he afterwards found that he had been anticipated by C. F. Varley in 1860. Still later it was discovered that a similar instrument had been made a century before by Nicholson, and called by him the " Revolving Doubler."

The experiments which Thomson made on atmospheric electricity at the old College tower, and by means of portable electrometers in Arran and elsewhere, can only be mentioned. They led no doubt to some improvements on electrometers which he made, the method of bringing the nozzle of a water-dropper, or a point on a portable electrometer to the potential of the air, by the inductive action on a stream of water-drops in the one case, or the particles of smoke from a burning match in the other. He invented a self-acting machine, worked by a stream of water-drops, for accumulating electric charges, on the principle of the revolving doubler. It was this apparently that led to the machines with revolving carriers, to which reference has been made above.

The mathematical theory of magnetism which Thomson gave in 1849, in the *Phil. Trans. R.S.*, was, when completed by various later papers, a systematic discussion of the whole subject, including electromagnetism and diamagnetism. To a large extent the ground covered by the 1849 paper had been traversed before by Poisson, and partially by Murphy and Green; but Thomson stated that one chief object of his memoir was to formally construct the theory without reference to the two magnetic fluids, by means of which the facts of experiment and conclusions of theory had so far been expressed. He found it, however, convenient to introduce the idea of positive and negative magnetic matter (attracting and repelling as do charges of positive and negative electricity), which are to be regarded as always present in equal amounts, not only in a magnet as a whole, but in every portion of a magnet ; and at first sight this might appear like a return to the magnetic fluids. But it amounts on the whole rather to a conception of a magnet as a conglomeration of doublets of magnetic matter (that is, very close, equal and inseparable charges of the two kinds of matter), the arrangement of which can be changed by the action of magnetic force. This idea is set forth now in all the books on magnetism and electricity. There can be no doubt that the systematic presentment of the subject by Thomson, and the theorems and ideas of magnetic force and magnetic permeability by which he rendered the clear, and therefore mathematical, notions of Faraday explicitly quantitative, had much influence in furthering the progress of electrical science, and so leading on the one hand to the electromagnetic theories of Maxwell, and on the other to modern research on the magnetic properties of iron, and to the correct ideas which now prevail as to construction of dynamo-electric machines and motors.

CHAPTER XII

THE AGE OF THE EARTH

FROM his student days throughout his life, Lord Kelvin took a keen interest in geological questions. He was always an active member of the Geological Society of Glasgow, and was its president for twenty-one years (1872–1883). The distribution of heat in the substance of the earth was the subject of his inaugural dissertation as Professor of Natural Philosophy ; and previously, as a student, he had written an essay on "The Figure of the Earth," for which he had been awarded a University Gold Medal. He never ceased to ponder over the problems of terrestrial physics, and he wrote much on the subject. His papers are to be found as Appendices to Thomson and Tait's *Natural Philosophy*, and in vol. ii of his *Popular Lectures and Addresses*, which is devoted to geology and general physics.

His conclusions regarding the age of the earth have been referred to in the last chapter. The first allusion to the subject was contained (see p. 65 above) in his inaugural dissertation "*De Caloris distributione in Terræ Corpus*" ; but he returned to it again in a communication made to the Royal Society of Edinburgh in December, 1865, and entitled "The Doctrine of Uniformity in Geology briefly refuted." On February 27, 1868, he delivered to the Geological Society of

Glasgow an address entitled "On Geological Time," in which the necessity for limiting geological and other changes to an almost infinitesimal fraction of the vast periods at that time demanded was insisted on, and which gave rise to much discussion.

The address began with a protest against the old uniformitarian view of geological changes as expressed by Playfair in his *Illustrations of the Huttonian Theory*. The first objection taken to the idea that "in the continuation of the different species of animals and vegetables that inhabit the earth, we discern neither a beginning nor an end; in the planetary motions where geometry has carried the eye so far, both into the future and the past, we discover no mark either of the commencement or the termination of the present order" is, that the stability of the motions of the heavenly bodies, to which reference is made in this statement, is founded upon what is essentially an approximate calculation, which leaves out, by intention, the consideration of frictional resistance.

He points out, for example, that the friction which accompanies the relative motion of the waters of the earth and the land is attended by the production of heat, and that, by the doctrine of the conservation of energy, heat cannot be produced without a disappearance of an equivalent quantity of energy, either of motion or of position. The chief source of this energy is the earth's rotation. Since the earth turns under the moon and the tidal spheroid—that is, the earth's shape as distorted by the heaping up of the waters in the tides—remains on the whole stationary with respect to the moon, the solid matter of the earth turns under the distribution of the water, held

more or less fixed by the moon, as does a fly-wheel
under a stationary friction band round its rim. Then
just as the band held fixed retards the fly-wheel, so
the earth must be retarded in its rotation by this
water-brake. In the earth's rotation there is a store
of kinetic energy which, roughly estimated, would not
be exhausted in less than ten million million years,
although drawn upon continuously by friction, or
other actions, at the rate of one million horse-power ;
so that, no immediate catastrophe, such as that we
should be involved in by the stoppage or considerable
retardation of the spinning motion of the earth, is
possible. But it was pointed out by Thomson that
the best results of astronomical observation show that
the earth would in one hundred years fall behind a
perfect time-keeper, with which its rotation kept pace
at the beginning of the time, by about twenty seconds.
The tendency is to make the earth turn slower, and
the moon to increase its distance and move more slowly
in its orbit, but with a resultant effect towards coincidence of the period of the earth's rotation with that of
revolution of the moon round the earth. After this
coincidence has been attained, however, the solar tides
will tend to make the moon fall in towards the earth.

If then the earth be rotating more and more slowly,
as time goes on, at present, it must have been rotating
more rapidly in past time. A thousand million years
ago, at the present rate of retardation, the earth must
have been rotating one seventh part of its speed faster
than it is rotating at present, and this would give for
centrifugal force at the surface one thousand million
years ago, greater than the centrifugal force at present,
in the ratio of 64 to 49. Apparently therefore the

earth must have solidified at a much later date than that epoch, a date when it was rotating much more nearly with the angular speed which it has now ; otherwise the figure of the earth would have deviated much more from the spherical form than it actually does.　On the other hand, one hundred million years ago centrifugal force would be only three per cent. greater than it is at present, and consolidation of the earth at that less remote period would give a shape to the earth not very different from that which it now possesses.　The argument therefore from tidal retardation would cut down the time available for geological and biological changes to something not much more than one hundred million years, perhaps to less.

A second argument for limitation of the time available for such processes is derived from the sun's heat. The sun cannot be regarded as a miraculous body producing its light and heat from nothing.　Changes of the constitution of the sun must be continually proceeding, to account for its enormous radiation of energy into space, a radiation of which only an infinitesimal part is received by the bodies of the solar system, and a still more minute portion by the earth. The effects of the sun's light and heat on the earth show how enormous must be the quantity of energy lost from the sun in a year.　How is this loss of energy to be accounted for ? what is the physical change which gives rise to it ?　In 1854 Thomson put forward the theory that the sun's heat is kept up by the falling in of meteors on the sun's surface, but he afterwards saw reason to abandon that view.　Helmholtz had advocated the theory that the sun was a body heated by the coming together of the matter composing it by its mutual attraction, a process which, although the sun is now a continuous mass, is to be regarded as still going on. It is easy to calculate the exhaustion of potential energy caused by the coming together of the matter of the sun from universal dispersion through infinite space to a sphere of uniform density of the present size of the sun. The result is about as much energy as would be generated by burning seven million million million million million tons of coal. The amount radiated in each hour is about as much as would be generated by burning something like nine tons of coal every hour on every square yard of the sun's surface. It is certain that the sun must be still contracting, and if it contracts sufficiently to just make good this expenditure by the further exhaustion of potential energy involved in the closer aggregation of the matter, it must diminish in radius in each year by as much as 130 feet.

The amount of energy generated by the falling together of the matter of the sun from universal diffusion to the dimensions which the sun has at present, is only about 13,000,000 times the amount now radiated per annum. In Thomson's paper Pouillet's estimate of the energy radiated per second is used, and this number is raised to 20,000,000. Taking the latter estimate, the whole potential energy exhausted by the condensation of the sun's mass to uniform density would suffice for only 20,000,000 years' supply. But the sun is undoubtedly of much greater density in the central parts than near the surface, and so the energy exhausted must be much greater than that stated above. This will raise the number of years provided for. On the other hand, a considerable amount of energy would be dissipated during the process of condensation, and this would reduce the period of radiation estimated. Thomson suggests that 50,000,000, or 100,000,000, years is a possible estimate.

It is not unlikely that the rate of radiation in past time, when the sun had not nearly condensed to its present size, was so much less than it is at present that the period suggested above may have to be considerably augmented. Another source of radiation, which seems to be regarded by some authorities as a probable, if not a certain, one, has been suggested in recent years—the presence of radio-active substances in the sun. So far as we know, Lord Kelvin did not admit that this source of radiation was worthy of consideration ; but of course, granted its existence to an extent comparable with the energy derivable from condensation of the sun's mass, the "age of the sun's heat" would have to be very greatly extended. These are matters, however, on which further light may be thrown as research in radio-activity progresses. Lord Kelvin was engaged when seized with his last illness in discussing the changes of energy in a gaseous, or partially gaseous, globe, slowly cooling and shrinking in doing so ; and a posthumous paper on the subject will shortly be published which may possibly contain further information on this question of solar physics.

But Thomson put forward a third argument in the paper on Geological Time, which has always been regarded as the most important. It is derived from the fact, established by abundant observations, that the temperature in the earth's crust increases from the surface inwards ; and that therefore the earth must be

continually losing heat by conduction from within.   If
the earth be supposed to have been of uniform temperature at some period of past time and in a molten
state, and certain assumptions as to the conductive
power and melting point of its material be made, the
time of cooling until the gradient of temperature at the
surface acquired its present value can be calculated.
This was done by Thomson in a paper published in the
Transactions, *R.S.E.*, in 1862.   We propose to give
here a short sketch of his argument, which has excited
much interest, and been the cause of some controversy.

In order to understand this argument, the reader
must bear in mind some fundamental facts of the flow
of heat in a solid.   Let him imagine a slab of any
uniform material, say sandstone or marble, the two
parallel faces of which are continually maintained at
two different temperatures, uniform over each face.
For example, steam may be continually blown against
one face, while ice-cold water is made to flow over the
other.   Heat will flow across the slab from the hotter
face to the colder.   It will be found that the rate of
flow of heat per unit area of face, that is per square
centimetre, or per square inch, is proportional to the
difference of the temperatures in the slab at the two
faces, and inversely proportional to the thickness of the
slab.   In other words, it is proportional to the fall of
temperature from one face to the other taken per unit
of the thickness, that is, to the " gradient of temperature " from one face to the other.   Moreover, comparing the flow in one substance with the flow in
another, we find it different in different substances for
the same gradient of temperature.   Thus we get
finally a flow of heat across unit area of the slab which

is equal to the gradient of temperature multiplied by a number which depends on the material : that number is called the " conductivity " of the substance.

Now, borings made in the earth show that the temperature increases inwards, and the same thing is shown by the higher temperatures found in deeper coal mines. By means of thermometers sunk to different depths, the rate of increase of temperature with depth has been determined. Similar observations show that the daily and annual variations of temperature caused by the succession of day and night, and summer and winter, penetrate to only a comparatively small depth below the surface—three or four feet in the former case, sixty or seventy in the latter. Leaving these variations out of account, since the average of their effects over a considerable interval of time must be nothing, we have in the earth a body at every point of the crust of which there is a gradient of increasing temperature inwards. The amount of this may be taken as one degree of Fahrenheit's scale for every 50 feet of descent. This gradient is not uniform, but diminishes at greater depths. Supposing the material of uniform quality as regards heat-conducting power, the mathematical theory of a cooling globe of solid material (or of a straight bar which does not lose heat from its sides) gives on certain suppositions the gradients at different depths. The surface gradient of 1° F. in 50 feet may be taken as holding for 5000 feet or 6000 feet or more.

This gradient of diminution of temperature outwards leads inevitably to the conclusion that heat must be constantly flowing from the interior of the earth towards the surface. This is as certain as that heat flows along a poker, one end of which is in the fire, from the heated end to the other. The heat which arrives at the surface of the earth is radiated to the atmosphere or carried off by convection currents ; there is no doubt that it is lost from the earth. Thus the earth must be cooling at a rate which can be calculated on certain assumptions, and it is possible on these assumptions to calculate backwards, and determine the interval of time which must have elapsed since the earth was just beginning to cool from a molten condition, when of course life cannot have existed on its surface, and those geological changes which have effected so much can hardly have began.

Considering a globe of uniform material, and of great radius, which was initially at one temperature, and at a certain instant had its surface suddenly brought to, let us say, the temperature of melting ice, at which the surface was kept ever after, we can find, by Fourier's mathematical theory of the flow of heat, the gradient of temperature at any subsequent time for a point on the surface, or at any specified distance within it. For a point on the surface this gradient is simply proportional to the initial uniform temperature, and inversely proportional to the square root of the product of the " diffusivity " of the material (the ratio of the conductivity to the specific heat) by the interval of time which has elapsed since the cooling was started. Taking a foot as the unit of length, and a year as the unit of time, we find the diffusivity of the surface strata to be 400. If we take the initial temperature as 7000 degrees F.—which is high enough for melting rock—and take the interval of time which has elapsed as 100,000,000 years, we obtain at the surface a gradient approximately equal to that which now exists. A greater interval of time would give a lower gradient, a smaller interval would give a higher gradient than that which exists at present. A lower initial temperature would require a smaller interval of time, a higher initial temperature a longer interval for the present gradient.

With the initial temperature of 7,000 degrees F., an interval of 4,000,000 years would give a surface gradient of 1° F. in 10 ft. Thus, on the assumption made, the surface gradient of temperature has diminished from $\frac{1}{10}$ to $\frac{1}{50}$ in about 96,000,000 years. After 10,000 years from the beginning of the cooling the gradient of temperature would be 2° F. per foot. But, as Thomson showed, such a large gradient would not lead to any sensible augmentation of the surface temperature, for " the radiation from earth and atmosphere into space would almost certainly be so rapid" as to prevent this. Hence he inferred that conducted heat, even at that early period, could not sensibly affect the general climate.

Two objections (apart from the assumptions already indicated) will readily occur to any one considering this theory, and these Thomson answered by anticipation. The first is, that no natural action could possibly bring the surface of a uniformly heated globe instantaneously to a temperature 7000° lower, and keep it so ever after. In reply to this Thomson urged "that a large mass of melted rock, exposed freely to our earth and sky, will, after it once becomes crusted over, present in a few hours, or a few days, or at most a few weeks, a surface so cool that it can be walked over with impunity. Hence, after 10,000 years, or indeed, I may say, after a single year, its condition will be sensibly the same as if the actual lowering of temperature experienced by the surface had been produced in an instant, and maintained constant ever after." The other objection was, that the earth was probably never a uniformly heated solid 7000° F. above the present surface temperature as assumed for the purpose of calculation. This Thomson answers by giving reasons for believing that " the earth, although once all melted, or melted all round its surface, did, in all probability, really become a solid at its melting temperature all through, or all through the outer layer which has been melted ; and not until the solidification was thus complete, or nearly so, did the surface begin to cool."

Thomson was inclined to believe that a temperature of 7000° F. was probably too high, and results of experiments on the melting of basalt and other rocks led him to prefer a much reduced temperature. This, as has already been pointed out, would give a smaller value for the age of the earth. In a letter on the subject published in *Nature* (vol. 51, 1895) he states that he " is not led to differ much " from an estimate of 24,000,000 years founded by Mr. Clarence King (*American Journal of Science*, January 1893) on experiments on the physical properties of rocks at high temperatures.

It is to be observed that the assumptions made above that the physical constants of the material are constant throughout the earth, and at all temperatures, are confessedly far from the truth. Nevertheless Thomson strongly held that the uncertainty of the data can at most extend the earth's age to some value between 20,000,000 and 200,000,000 of years, and that the enormously long periods which were wont to be asked for by geologists and biologists for the changes of the earth's surface and the development of its flora and fauna, cannot possibly be conceded.

In *Nature* for January 3, 1895, Professor John Perry suggested that very possibly the conductivity of the material composing the interior of the earth was considerably higher than that of the surface strata. If this were so, then, as can be shown without difficulty, the attainment of the present gradient would be very greatly retarded, and therefore the age of the earth correspondingly increased. The question then arose, and was discussed, as to whether the rocks and other materials at high temperatures were more or less conducting than at low temperatures, and experiments on the subject were instituted and carried out. On the whole, the evidence seemed to show that the conductivity of most substances is diminished, not increased, by the rise of temperature, and so far as it went, therefore, the evidence was against Professor Perry's suggestion. On the other hand, he contended that the inside of the earth may be a mass of great rigidity, partly solid and partly fluid, possessing a "quasi-conductivity" which might greatly increase the period of cooling. The subject is a difficult one both from a mathematical and from the physical point of view, and further investigation is necessary, especially of the behaviour of materials under the enormous stresses which they undoubtedly sustain in the interior of the earth.

After the publication of the paper on Geological Time a reply to it was made by Professor Huxley, in an address to the Geological Society of London, delivered on February 19, 1869. He adopted the *rôle* of an advocate retained for the defence of geology against what seems to have been regarded as an unwarranted attack, made by one who had no right to offer an opinion on a geological question. For, after a long and eloquent "pleading," he concludes his address with the words : "My functions, as your advocate, are at an end. I speak with more than the sincerity of a mere advocate when I express the belief that the case against us has entirely broken down. The cry for reform which has been raised from without is superfluous, inasmuch as we have long been reforming from within with all needful speed ; and the critical examination of the grounds upon which the very grave charge of opposition to the principles of Natural Philosophy has been brought against us, rather shows that we have exercised a wise discrimination in declining to meddle with our foundations at the bidding of the first passer-by who fancies our house is not so well built as it might be." To this Thomson rejoined in an address entitled "Of Geological Dynamics," also delivered to the Geological Society of Glasgows on April 5, 1869 ; and to this, with Professor Huxley's address, the reader must be referred for the objection, brought against Thomson's arguments, and the replies which were immediately forthcoming. This is not the place to discuss the question, but reference may be made to an interesting paper on the subject in the *Glasgow Herald* for February 22, 1908, by Professor J. W. Gregory, in which the suggestion of Professor Perry, of a nearer approach to uniformity of temperature in the interior of the earth than Thomson had thought possible, is welcomed as possibly extending the interval of time available to a period sufficient for all purposes. In Professor Gregory's opinion, "Lord Kelvin in one respect showed a keener insight than Huxley, who, referring to possible changes in the rate of rotation of the earth, or in the heat given forth from the sun or in the cooling of the earth, declared that geologists are Gallios, 'who care for none of these things.' An ever-increasing school of geologists now cares greatly for these questions, and reveres Lord Kelvin as one of the founders of the geology of the inner earth."

After all, the problem is not one to be dealt with by the geologist or biologist alone, but to be solved, so far as it can be solved at all, by a consideration of all relevant evidence, from whatsoever quarter it may come. It will not do in these days for scientific men to shut themselves up within their special departments and to say, with regard to branches of science which deal with other aspects of nature and other problems of the past, present and future of that same earth on which all dwell and work, that they " care for none of these things." This is an echo of an old spirit, not yet dead, that has done much harm to the progress of science. The division of science into departments is unavoidable, for specialisation is imperative ; but it is all the more necessary to remember that the divisions set up are more or less arbitrary, and that there are absolutely no frontiers to be guarded and enforced. Chemistry, physiology, and physics cannot be walled off from one another without loss to all ; and geology has suffered immensely through its having been regarded as essentially a branch of natural history, the devotees of which have no concern with considerations of natural philosophy. Lord Kelvin's dignified questions were unanswerable. "Who are the occupants of ' our house,' and who is the 'passer-by'? Is geology not a branch of physical science? Are investigations, experimental and mathematical, of underground temperature not to be regarded as an integral part of geology? . . . For myself, I am anxious to be regarded by geologists not as a mere passer-by, but as one constantly interested in their grand subject, and anxious in any way, however slight, to assist them in their search for truth."

CHAPTER XIII

WHEN Professor Thomson began his work as a teacher
in the University of Glasgow, there was, as has already
been noticed, great vagueness of specification of physical
quantities. Few of the formal definitions of units of
measurement, now to be found in the pages of every
elementary text book, had been framed, and there
was much confusion of quantities essentially distinct,
a confusion which is now, to some extent at least,
guarded against by the adoption of a definite unit,
with a distinctive name for each magnitude to be
measured. Thus rate of working, or activity, was
confused with work done ; the condition for maximum
activity in the circuit of a battery or dynamo was often
quoted as the condition of greatest efficiency, that is of
greatest economy of energy, although it was exactly
that in which half the available energy was wasted.

Partly as a consequence of this vagueness of specification, there was a great want of knowledge of the values
of physical constants ; for without exact definitions of
quantities to be determined, such definitions as would
indicate units for their measurement, related to ordinary
dynamical units according to a consistent scheme, it was
impossible to devise satisfactory experimental methods

to do for electricity and magnetism what had been done by Regnault and others for heat.

The first steps towards the construction of a complete system of units for the quantitative measurement of magnetic and electric quantities were taken by Gauss, in his celebrated paper entitled *Intensitas vis magneticæ terrestris ad mensuram absolutam revocata*, published in 1832. In this he showed how magnetic forces could be expressed in absolute units, and thus be connected with the absolute dynamical units which Gauss, in the same paper, based on chosen fundamental units of length, mass, and time. Thus the modern system of absolute units of dynamical quantities, and its extension to magnetism, are due to the practical insight of a great mathematician, not to the experimentalists or "practicians" of the time.

Methods of measuring electric quantities in absolute units were described by W. Weber, in Parts II and III of his *Elecktrodynamische Maassbestimmungen*, published in 1852. These were great steps in advance, and rendered further progress in the science of absolute measurement comparatively easy. But they remained the only steps taken until the British Association Committee began their work. We have already (pp. 74–76) referred to the great importance of that work, not only for practical applications but also for the advancement of science. But it was not a task which struck the imagination or excited the wonder of the multitude. For the realisation of standards of resistance, for example, involved long and tedious investigations of the effects of impurities on the resistance of metals, and the variation of resistance caused by change of temperature and lapse of time. Then alloys had to be sought which would have a temperature effect of small amount, and which were stable and durable in all their properties.

The discoveries of the experimentalist who finds a new element of hitherto undreamed-of properties attract world-wide attention, and the glory of the achievement is deservedly great. But the patient, plodding work which gives a universal system of units and related standards, and which enables a great physical subject like electricity and magnetism to rise from a mere enumeration of qualitative results to a science of the most delicate and exact measurement, and to find its practical applications in all the affairs of daily life and commerce, is equally deserving of the admiration and gratitude of mankind. Yet it receives little or no recognition.

The construction of a standard of resistance was the first task undertaken by the committee; but other units, for example of quantity of electricity, intensity of electric field and difference of potential, had also to be defined, and methods of employing them in experimental work devised. It would be out of place to endeavour to discuss these units here, but some idea of the manner in which their definitions are founded on dynamical conceptions may be obtained from one or two examples. Therefore we shall describe two simple experiments, which will illustrate this dynamical foundation. An account has been given in Chapter XI of the series of electrometers which Thomson invented for the measurement of differences of electric potential. These all act by the evaluation in terms of ordinary dynamical units of the force urging an electrified body from a place of higher towards a place of lower potential.

Some indication of the meaning of electrical quantities has been given in Chapter IV. Difference of electric potential between two points in an electric field was there defined as the dynamical work done in carrying a unit of positive electricity against the forces of the field from the point of lower to the point of higher potential. Now by the definition of unit quantity of electricity given in electrical theory—that quantity which, concentrated at a point at unit distance from an equal quantity also concentrated at a point, is repelled with unit force—we can find, by the simple experiment of hanging two pith balls (or, better, two hollow, gilded beads of equal size) by two fine fibres of quartz, a metre long, say, electrifying the two balls as they hang in contact, and observing the distance at which they then hang, the numerical magnitude in absolute units of a charge of electricity, and apply that to finding the charge on a large spherical conductor and the potential at points in its field also in absolute units. If m be the mass of a ball, g gravity in cm. sec. units, d the distance in cms. of the centres of the balls apart, and l the length in cms. of a thread, the charge q, say, on each ball is easily found to be $\sqrt{mgd^3} / \sqrt{4l^2 - d^2}$. Thus the charge is got in absolute centimetre-gramme-second units in terms of the mass m obtained by ordinary weighing, and l and d obtained by easy and exact measurements.

If one of the balls be now taken away without discharging the other, and the latter be placed in the field of a large electrified spherical conductor, the fibre will be deflected from the vertical by the force on the ball. Let the two centres be now on the same level. That force is got at once from the angle of deflection (which is easily observed), the charge on the ball, and the value of m. The electric field-intensity is obtained by dividing the value of the force by q. The field intensity multiplied by D, the distance apart in cms. of the centres of the ball and the conductor, gives the potential at the centre of the ball in C.G.S. units. Multiplication again by D gives the charge on the conductor.

When it made its first Report in 1862 (to the meeting at Cambridge) the committee consisted of Professors A. Williamson, C. Wheatstone, W. Thomson, W. H. Miller, Dr. A. Matthiessen, and Mr. F. Jenkin. At the next meeting, at Newcastle, it had been augmented by the addition of Messrs. Balfour Stewart, C. W. Siemens, Professor Clerk Maxwell, Dr. Joule, Dr. Esselbach, and Sir Charles Bright. The duty with which the committee had been charged was that of constructing a suitable standard of resistance. A reference to the account given in Chapter X above, of the derivation of what came to be called the electromagnetic unit of difference of potential, or electromotive force, by means of a simple magneto-electric machine—a disk turning on a uniform magnetic field, or the simple rails and slider and magnetic field arrangement there described—will show how from this unit and the electromagnetic unit of current (there also defined) the unit of resistance is defined. It is the resistance of the circuit of slider, rails, and connecting wire, when with this electromagnetic unit of electromotive force the unit of current is made to flow.

This was one clear and definite way of defining the unit of current, and of attaining the important object of connecting the units in such a way that the rate of working in a circuit, or the energy expended in any time, should be expressed at once in ordinary dynamical units of activity or energy. A considerable number of proposals were discussed by the committee ; but it was finally determined to take the basis here indicated, and to realise a standard of resistance in material of constant and durable properties, which should have some simple multiple of the unit of resistance, in the system of dynamical units based on the centimetre as unit of length, the gramme as unit of mass, and the second as unit of time—the so-called C.G.S. system. The comparison of the different metals and alloys available was a most important but exceedingly laborious series of investigations, carried out mainly by Dr. Matthiessen and Professor Williamson.

Professor Thomson suggested to the committee the celebrated method of determining the resistance of a circuit by revolving a coil, which formed the main part of the circuit about a vertical axis in the earth's magnetic field. An account of the experiments made with this method is contained in the Report of 1863. They were carried out at King's College, London, where Maxwell was then Professor of Experimental Physics, by Maxwell, Balfour Stewart, and Fleeming Jenkin. The theoretical discussion and the description of the experiments was written by Maxwell, the details of the apparatus were described by Jenkin.

The principle of the method is essentially the same as that of the simple magneto-electric machine, to which reference has just been made. Two parallel coils of wire were wound in channels cut round rings of brass, which, however, were cut across by slots filled with vulcanite, to prevent induced currents from circulating in the brass. These coils were mounted in a vertical position and could be driven as a rigid system, at a constant measured speed, about a vertical

axis passing through the centre of the system. Between
the coils at this centre was hung, from a steady support,
a small magnetic needle by a single fibre of silk ; and a
surrounding screen prevented the needle and suspension
from being affected by currents of air.

The ends of the coil were connected together so
that the whole revolved as a closed circuit about the
vertical axis. When the coil system was at right
angles to the magnetic meridian there was a magnetic
induction through it of amount AH, where A denotes
the effective area of the coils, and H the horizontal
component of the earth's magnetic field. By one
half-turn the coil was reversed with reference to this
magnetic induction, and as the coil turned an induced
current was generated, which depended at any instant
on the rate at which the magnetic induction was varying at the instant, on the inductive electromotive force
due to the varying of the current in the coil itself, and
on the resistance of the circuit. A periodic current
thus flowed in one direction *relatively to the coil* in one
half-turn from a position perpendicular to the magnetic
meridian, and in the opposite direction in the next
half-turn. But as the position of the coil was reversed
in every half-turn as well as the current in it, the current
flowed on the whole in the same average direction
relatively to the needle, and but for self-induction
would have had its maximum value always when the
plane of the coil was in the magnetic meridian.

The needle was deflected as it would have been
by a certain average current, and the deflection was
opposed by the action of the earth's horizontal magnetic field H. But this was the field cut by the coil
as it turned, and therefore (except for a small term

depending on the turning of the coil in the field of the needle) the value of H did not appear in the result, and did not require to be known.

Full details of the theory of this method and of the experiments carried out to test it will be found in various memoirs and treatises [1] ; but it must suffice here to state that the resistance of the coil was determined in this way, by a large series of experiments, before and after every one of which the resistance was compared with that of a German-silver standard. The resistance of this standard therefore became known in absolute units, and copies of it, or multiples or sub-multiples of it, could be made.

A unit called the B.A. unit, which was intended to contain 10^9 C.G.S. electromagnetic units of resistance, was constructed from these experiments, and copies of it were soon after to be found in nearly all the physical laboratories of the world. Resistance boxes were constructed by various makers, in which the coils were various multiples of the B.A. unit, so that any resistance within a certain range could be obtained by connecting these coils in series (which was easily done by removing short circuiting plugs), and thus the absolute units of current electromotive force and resistance came into general use.

In 1881 Lord Rayleigh and Professor Schuster carried out a very careful repetition of the British Association experiments with the same apparatus at the Cavendish Laboratory, and obtained a somewhat different result. They found that the former result

---

[1] See the *Reports of the Committee on Electrical Standards,* edited by Prof. Fleeming Jenkin, F.R.S., Maxwell's *Electricity and Magnetism,* and Gray's *Theory and Practice of Absolute Measurements in Electricity and Magnetism,* Vol. II, Part II.

was about 1·17 per cent. too small. Lord Rayleigh next carried out an independent set of experiments by the same method with improved apparatus, and found that this percentage error must be increased to about 1·35.

It may be noticed here that the simple disk machine, of Thomson's illustration of the absolute unit of electromotive force, has been used by Lorenz to give a method of determining resistance which is now recognised as the best of all. It is sketched here that the reader may obtain some idea of later work on this very important subject ; work which is a continuation of that of the original British Association Committee by their successors. A circuit is made up of a standard coil of wire, the ends of which are made to touch at the circumference and near the centre of the disk, which is placed symmetrically with respect to a cylindrical coil, and within it. A current is sent round this coil from a battery, and produces a magnetic field within the coil, the lines of magnetic force of which pass across the plane of the disk. This current, or a measured fraction of it, is also made to flow through the standard coil. The disk is now turned at a measured speed about its axis, so that the electromotive force due to the cutting of the field tends to produce a current in the standard coil of wire. The electromotive force of the disk is made to oppose the potential difference between the ends of this coil due to the current, so that no current flows along the disk or the wires connecting it with the standard coil. The magnetic field within the coil can be calculated from the form and dimensions of the coil and the current in it (supposed for the moment to be known), and the electromotive force of the disk is obtained in terms of its dimensions and its speed and the field intensity. But this electro-motive force, which is proportional to the current in the coil, is equal to the product of the resistance of the wire and the same current, or a known fraction of it. Thus the current appears on both sides of the equation and goes out, and the value of the resistance is found in absolute units.

Lord Rayleigh obtained, by this method, a result which showed that the B.A. unit was 1·323 per cent. too small; and exact experiments have been made by others with concordant results. Values of the units have been agreed on by International Congresses as exact enough for general work, and with these units all electrical researches, wherever made, are available for use by other experimenters.

A vast amount of work has been done on this subject during the last forty years, and though the value of the practical unit of resistance—10^9 C.G.S. units, now called the "ohm"—is taken as settled, and copies can now be had in resistance boxes, or separately, adjusted with all needful accuracy, at the National Physical Laboratory and at the Bureau of Standards at Washington, and elsewhere, experiments are being made on the exact measurement of currents; while a careful watch is kept on the standards laid up at these places to see whether any perceptible variation of their resistance takes place with lapse of time.

The British Association Committee also worked out a complete system of units for all electrical and mag-netic quantities, and gave the first systematic statement of their relations, that is, of the so-called dimensional equations of the quantities. This will be found in the works to which reference has already been made (p. 251).

CHAPTER XIV

THE BALTIMORE LECTURES

THE Baltimore Lectures were delivered in 1884 at Johns Hopkins University, soon after the Montreal meeting of the British Association. The subject chosen was the Wave Theory of Light; and the idea underlying the course was to discuss the difficulties of this theory to "Professorial fellow-students in physical science." A stenographic report of the course was taken by Mr. A. S. Hathaway, and was published soon after. The lectures were revised by Lord Kelvin, and the book now known as *The Baltimore Lectures* was published just twenty years later (in 1904) at the Cambridge University Press. It is absolutely impossible in such a memoir as the present to give any account of the discussions contained in the lectures as now published. The difficulties dealt with can for the most part only be understood by those who are acquainted with the wave theory of light in its details, and such readers will naturally go direct to the book itself.

Some of the difficulties, however, were frequently alluded to in Lord Kelvin's ordinary lectures, and all his old students will remember the animation with which he discussed the apparent anomaly of a medium like the luminiferous ether, which is of such enormous rigidity that (on the elastic solid theory) a wave of transverse oscillation is propagated through it with a speed of

3×10^{10} centimetres (186,000 miles) per second, and yet appears to offer no impediment to the slow motion of the heavenly bodies. For Lord Kelvin adopted the elastic solid theory of propagation of light as " the only tenable foundation for the wave theory of light in the present state of our knowledge," and dismissed the electromagnetic theory (his words were spoken in 1884, it is to be remembered) with the statement of his strong view that an electric displacement perpendicular to the line of propagation, accompanied by a magnetic disturbance at right angles to both, is inadmissible.

And he goes on to say that " when we have an electromagnetic theory of light," electric displacement will be seen as in the direction of propagation, with Fresnelian vibrations perpendicular to that direction. In the preface, of date January 1904, the insufficiency of the elastic solid theory is admitted, and the question of the electromagnetic theory again referred to.   He says there that the object of the Baltimore Lectures was to ascertain how far the phenomena of light could be explained within the limits of the elastic solid theory. And the answer is " everything *non-magnetic ; nothing magnetic.*"   But he adds, " The so-called electromagnetic theory of light has not helped us hitherto," and that the problem is now fully before physicists of constructing a " comprehensive dynamics of ether, electricity, and ponderable matter which shall include electrostatic force, magnetostatic force, electromagnetism, electrochemistry, and the wave theory of light."

All this is exceedingly interesting, for it seems to make clear Lord Kelvin's attitude with respect to the electromagnetic theory of Maxwell, which is now regarded by most physicists as affording on the whole a satisfactory account, if not a dynamical theory in the sense understood by Lord Kelvin, of light-propagation. That there is an electric displacement perpendicular to the direction of propagation and a magnetic displacement (or motion) perpendicular to both seems proved by the experiments of Hertz, and the velocity of propagation of these disturbances has been found to be that of light. Of course it remains to be found out in what the electric and magnetic changes consist, and whether the ether has or has not an atomic structure. Towards the answer to this question on electromagnetic presuppositions some progress has already been made, principally by Larmor. And, after all, while we may imagine that we know something more definite of dynamical actions on ponderable matter, it is not quite certain that we do : we are more familiar with them, that is almost all. We know, for example, that at every point in the gravitational field of the earth we may set up a gravitation vector, or field-intensity ; for a particle of matter there is subjected to acceleration along that direction. But of the *rationale* of the action we know nothing, or next to nothing. So we set up electric and magnetic vectors in an insulating medium, corresponding to electric and magnetic effects which we can observe ; and it is not too much to say that we know hardly less in this case than we do in the other, of the inner mechanism of the action of which we see the effects.

Returning to the difficulty of the elastic solid theory, that while its rigidity is enormous, it offers no obstacle to the planets and other heavenly bodies which move through it, it may be interesting to recall how Lord

Kelvin used to deal with it in his elementary lectures. The same discussion was given in the Introductory Lecture at Baltimore. The difficulty is not got over by an explanation of what takes place : it is turned by showing that a similar difficulty exists in reconciling phenomena which can be observed every day with such ordinary materials as pitch or shoemakers' wax. A piece of such wax can be moulded into a tuning-fork or a bell, and will then, if struck, sound a musical note of definite pitch. This indicates, for rapidly alternating deformations started by a force of short duration, the existence of internal forces of the kind called elastic, that is, depending on the amount of deformation caused, not on the rate at which the deformation is increasing or diminishing, as is the case for the so-called " viscous forces " which are usually displayed by such material. But the tuning-fork or bell, if left lying on the table, will gradually flatten down into a thin sheet under only its own weight. Here the deformation is opposed only by viscous forces, which, as the change is very slow, are exceedingly small.

But let a large slab of it, three or four inches thick, be placed in a glass jar ten or twelve inches in diameter, already partly filled with water, and let some ordinary corks be imprisoned beneath, while some lead bullets are laid on the upper surface. After a month or two it will be found that the corks have disappeared from the water into the wax, and that the orifices which they made in entering it have healed up completely ; similarly the bullets have sunk down into the slab, leaving no trace behind. After two or three months more, the corks will be seen to be bursting their way out through the upper surface of the slab, and the

bullets will be found in the water below.   The very
thing has taken place that would have happened if
water had been used instead of pitch, only it has taken
a very much longer time to bring it about.   The corks
have floated up through the wax in consequence of
hydrostatic upward force exerted by the wax acting as a
fluid ; and the bullets have sunk down in consequence
of the excess of their weights above the upward
hydrostatic force exerted on them as on the corks.
The motion in both cases has been opposed by the
viscous forces called into play.

The application of this to the luminiferous ether is
immediate.   Let the ether be regarded as a substance
which can perform vibrations only " when times and
forces are suitable," that is, when the forces producing
distortion act for only an infinitesimal time (as in the
starting of the tuning-fork by a small blow), and are
not too great.   Vibrations may be set up locally, and
the medium may have a true rigidity by which they
are propagated to more remote parts ; that is to say,
waves travel out from the centre of disturbance.   On
the other hand, if the forces are long continued, even if
they be small, they produce continuously increasing
change of shape.   Thus the planets move seemingly
without resistance.

The conclusion is that the apparently contradictory
properties of the ether are no more mysterious than the
properties of pitch or shoemakers' wax.   And, after all,
matter is still a profound mystery.

Dynamical illustrations, which old Glasgow students
will recognise, appear continually in the lectures.
They will remember, almost with affection, the system
of three *particles* (7 lb. or 14 lb. weights !) joined

together in a vertical row by stout spiral springs of steel, which were always to be taken as massless, and will recall Lord Kelvin's experiments with them, demonstrating the three modes of vibration of a system of three masses, each of which influenced those next it on the two sides. Here they will find the problem solved for any number of particles and intervening springs, and the solution applied to an extension of the massive molecule which von Helmholtz imbedded in the elastic ether, and used to explain anomalous dispersion. A highly complex molecule is suggested, consisting of an outer shell embedded in the ether as in the simpler case, a second shell within that connected to the outer by a sufficient number of equal radial springs, a third within and similarly connected to the second by radial springs, and so on. This molecule will have as many modes of vibration as there are sets of springs, and can therefore impart, if it is set into motion, a complex disturbance to the ether in which it is imbedded.

The modification of this arrangement by which Lord Kelvin explained the phosphorescence of such substances as luminous paint is also described, and will be recognised by some as an old friend. A number, two dozen or so, of straight rods of wood eighteen inches long are attached to a steel wire four or five inches apart, like steps on a ladder made with a single rope along the centres of the steps. The wire is so attached to each rod that the rod must turn with the wire if the latter is twisted round. Each rod is loaded with a piece of lead at each end to give it more moment of inertia about the wire. The wire, with this "ladder" attached to it, is rigidly attached to the centre of a cross-bar at the top, which can be made to

swing about the wire as an axis and so impart twisting
vibrations to the wire in a period depending on this
driver.   Sliding weights attached to the bar enable its
moment of inertia to be changed at pleasure.   The
lower end of the wire carries a cross-bar with two
vanes, immersed in treacle in a vessel below.   When
the period of the exciter was very long the waves of

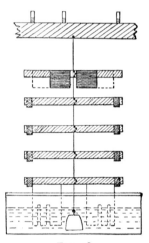

FIG. 18.

torsion did not travel down the " ladder," but when
the period was made sufficiently short the waves
travelled down and were absorbed in the treacle below.
In the former case the vibrations persisted ; the case
was analogous to that of phosphorescence.

Incidentally a full and very attractive account of the
elastic solid theory is given in these lectures, accompanied as it is by characteristic digressions on points of

interest which suggest themselves, and on topics on which the lecturer held strong opinions, such, for example, as the absurd British system of weights and measures. The book reads in many places like a report of some of the higher mathematical lectures which were given every session at Glasgow ; and on that account, if on no other, it will be read by the old students of the higher class with affectionate interest. But the discussions of the great fundamental difficulty presented at once by dispersion—the fact, that is, that light of different wave lengths has different velocities in ordinary transparent matter—the discussions of the various theories of dispersion that have been put forward, the construction of the molecules, gyrostatic and non-gyrostatic, with all their remarkable properties, which Lord Kelvin invents in order to frame a dynamical mechanism which will imitate the action of matter as displayed in the complex manifestations of the optical phenomena, not only of isotropic matter, but of crystals, will ever afford instruction to every mathematician who has the courage to attack this subject, and remain as a monument to the extraordinary genius of their author.

A subject is touched on in these lectures which has not been dealt with in the present review of Lord Kelvin's work. By four lines of argument—by the heat of combination of copper and zinc, together with the difference of electric potential developed when these metals are put in contact, from the thickness of a capillary film of soap and water (measured by Rücker and Reinold) just before it gives way, and the work spent in stretching it, from the kinetic theory of gases and the estimated length of free path of a particle (given also by

Loschmidt and by Johnstone Stoney), and from the undulatory theory of light—Lord Kelvin estimated superior and inferior limits to the "size of the atoms" of bodies, or, more properly speaking, of the molecular structure of the matter. We cannot discuss these arguments—and they can be read at leisure by any one who will consult Volume I (Constitution of Matter) of Lord Kelvin's *Popular Lectures and Addresses*, for his Royal Institution Lecture on the subject, there given in full—but we may state his conclusion. Let a drop of water, a rain drop, for example, be magnified to the size of the earth, that is, from a sphere a quarter of an inch, or less, in diameter to a sphere 8000 miles in diameter, and let the dimensions of the molecular structure be magnified in the same proportion. "The magnified structure would be more coarse-grained than a heap of small shot, but probably less coarse-grained than a heap of cricket-balls."

Of course, it is not intended here to convey the idea that the molecules are spheres like shot or cricket-balls; they undoubtedly have a structure of their own. And no pronouncement is made as to the divisibility or non-divisibility of the molecules. All that is alleged is that if the division be carried to a minuteness near to or beyond that of the dimensions of the structure, portions of the substance will be obtained which have not the physical properties of the substance in bulk.

The recent interesting researches of chemists and physicists into phenomena which seem to demonstrate the disintegration, not merely of molecules, but even of the atomic structure of matter, attracted Lord Kelvin's attention in his last years, and *suo more* he endeavoured to frame dynamical explanations of electronic (or, as he preferred to call it, "electrionic") action. But though keenly interested in all kinds of research, he turned again and again to the older theories of light, and his dynamical representations of the ether and of crystals, with renewed vigour and enthusiasm.

CHAPTER XV

THEORY OF SIGNALLING

WHEN the question of laying an Atlantic cable began to be debated in the middle of the nineteenth century, Professor Thomson undertook the discussion of the theory of signalling through such a cable. It was not generally understood by practical telegraphists that the conditions of working would be very different from those to which they were accustomed on land lines, and that the instruments employed on such lines would be useless for a cable. Such a cable consists of a copper conductor separated from the sea-water by a coating of gutta-percha ; it forms an elongated Leyden jar of very great capacity, which, when a battery is connected to one end of the conducting core, is gradually charged up, first at that end, and later and later at greater distances from it, and then is gradually discharged again when the battery is withdrawn and the end of the conductor connected to earth. Here, again, an application of Fourier's analysis solved the problem, which, with certain modifications, and on the supposition that the working is slow, is essentially the same problem as the diffusion of heat along a

264

conducting bar, or the diffusion of a salt solution
along a column of water. The signals are retarded
(and this was one of the results of the investigation)
in such a manner " that the time required to reach a
stated fraction of the maximum strength of current at
the remote end," when a given potential difference is
applied at the other, or home end, is proportional to
the product of the capacity and resistance of the cable,
each taken per unit of the length, and also proportional
to the square of the length of cable.   In other words,
the retardation is proportional to the product of the
resistance of the copper conductor and the total
capacity of the cable. This gave a practical rule of
great importance for guidance in the manufacture of
submarine cables. The conductor should have the
highest conductivity obtainable, and should therefore
be of pure copper ; the insulating covering should,
while forming a nearly absolutely non-conducting
sheath, have as low a specific inductive capacity as
possible.   The first of these conditions ran counter to
some views that had been put forward, to the effect
that it was only necessary to have the internal conductor highly conducting on its surface ; and some
controversy on the subject ensued. The inverse square
law, as it was called, was vehemently called in question,
from a mistaken interpretation of some experiments
that were made to test it. For if the potential at the
home end be regularly altered, according to the simple
harmonic law, so that the number of periods of oscillation in a second is n, the changes of potential are
propagated with velocity $2\sqrt{\pi n/cr}$, where c and r are
the capacity and resistance of the cable, each taken
per unit length.   In this case, for a long cable, there

is a velocity of propagation independent of the length ; and this fact seems to have misled the experimenters. Thomson's view prevailed, and the result was the establishment, first by Thomas Bolton & Sons, Stoke-on-Trent, of mills for the manufacture of high conductivity copper, which is now a great industry.

The Fourier mathematics of the conduction of heat along a bar suffices to solve the problem, so long as the signalling is so slow as not to bring into play electro-magnetic induction to any serious extent. For rapid signalling in which very quick changes of current are concerned the electromotive forces due to the growth or dying out of the current would be serious, and the theory of diffusion would not apply. But ordinary cable working is quite slow enough to enable such electromotive forces to be disregarded.

LAYING OF FIRST AMERICAN CABLES

The first cable of 1858 was laid by the U.S. frigate *Niagara* and H.M.S. *Agamemnon*, after having been manufactured with all the precautions suggested by Professor Thomson's researches. It is hard to realise how difficult such an enterprise was at the time. The manufacture of a huge cable, the stowage of it in cable tanks on board the vessels, the invention of laying and controlling and picking-up machinery had to be faced with but little experience to guide the engineers. Here again Thomson, by his knowledge of dynamics and true engineering instinct, was of great assistance. In 1865 he read a very valuable paper on the forces concerned in the laying and lifting of deep-sea cables, showing how the strains could be minimised in various practical cases of importance—for example, in the lifting of a cable for repairs.

A first Atlantic cable had been partly laid in 1857 by the *Niagara*, when it broke in 2000 fathoms of water, about 330 miles from Valentia, where the laying had begun. An additional length of 900 miles was made, and the enterprise was resumed. This time it was decided that the two vessels, each with half of the cable on board, should meet and splice the cable in mid-ocean, and then steam in opposite directions, the *Agamemnon* towards Valentia, the *Niagara* towards Newfoundland. Professor Thomson was engineer in charge of the electrical testing on board of the *Agamemnon*. After various mishaps the cable was at last safely laid on August 6, 1858, and congratulations were shortly after exchanged between Great Britain and the United States. On September 6 it was announced that signals had ceased to pass, and an investigation of the cause of the stoppage was undertaken by Professor Thomson and the other engineers. The report stated that the cable had been too hastily made, that, in fact, it was not good enough, and that the strains in laying it had been too great and unequal. It was found impossible to repair it, so that there was no option but to abandon it.

This cable probably suffered seriously from the violent means which seem to have been employed to force signals through it. Now only a very moderate difference of potential is applied to a cable at the sending end, and speed of signalling is obtained by the use of instruments, the moving parts of which have little inertia, and readily respond to only an exceedingly feeble current.

A second cable was made and laid in 1865 by the Great Eastern, which could take on board the whole at once and steam from shore to shore. It was also well adapted for cable work through having both screw and paddles. As Thomson points out, "steerage way" could be got on the vessel by driving the screw ahead, so as to send a stream of water astern towards the rudder, while the paddles were driven astern to prevent the ship from going ahead. This was of great advantage in manœuvring on many occasions.

This cable also broke, but a third was laid successfully in 1866 by the same vessel, and the second was recovered and repaired, so that two good cables were secured for commercial working. On both expeditions Professor Thomson acted as electrical engineer, and received the honour of knighthood and the thanks of the Anglo-American Telegraph Company on his return home, when he was also presented with the freedom of the city of Glasgow.

He afterwards acted as engineer for the French Atlantic Cable, for the Brazilian and River Plate Company, and for the Commercial Company, whose two new Atlantic cables were laid in 1882–4.

Mirror Galvanometer and Siphon Recorder

Since whatever the potential applied at the sending end of the cable might be (and, of course, as has been stated, this potential had to be kept to as low a value as possible) the current at the receiving end only rose gradually, it was necessary to have as delicate a receiving instrument as possible, so that it would quickly respond to the growing and still feeble current. For unless the cable could be worked at a rate which would permit of charges per word transmitted which were within the reach of commercial people, it was obvious that the enterprise would fail of its object. And as a cable could not cost less than half a million sterling, the revenue to be aimed at was very considerable. This problem Thomson also solved by the invention of his mirror galvanometer. The suspended magnet was made of small pieces of watch-spring cemented to a small mirror, so that the whole moving part weighed only a grain or two. Its inertia, or resistance to being set into motion, was thus very small, and it was hung by a single fibre of silk within a closed chamber at the centre of the galvanometer coil. A ray of light from a lamp was reflected to a white paper scale in front of the mirror, which as it turned caused a spot of illumination to move along the paper. A motion of this long massless index to the left was regarded as a dot, a motion to the right as a dash, and the Morse alphabet could therefore be employed. This instrument was used in the 1858 cable expedition, and a special form of suspension was invented for it by Thomson, to enable it to be used on board ship. The suspension thread, instead of being held at one end only, was stretched from top to bottom of the chamber in which the needle hung, and kept tight by being secured at both ends. Thus the minimum of disturbance was caused to the mirror by the rolling or pitching of the ship.

The galvanometer was also enclosed in a thick iron case to guard it against the magnetic field due to the iron of the ship. The "iron-clad galvanometer" first used in submarine telegraphy (on the 1858 expedition in the U.S. frigate *Niagara*) is in the collection of historical apparatus in the Natural Philosophy Department of the University of Glasgow.

The mirror galvanometer then invented has become one of the most useful instruments of the laboratory. Mirror deflection is now used also for the indicators of many kinds of instruments.

The galvanometer was replaced later by another invention of Professor Thomson—the siphon recorder. Here a small and delicate pen was formed by a piece of very fine glass tube (vaccination tubing, in fact) in the form of a siphon, of which the shorter end dipped into an ink-bottle, while the other end wrote the message in little zig-zag notches on a ribbon of paper drawn past it by machinery. The siphon was moved to and fro by the signalling currents, which flowed in a small coil hung between the poles of an electromagnet, excited by a local battery, and the ink was spirted in a succession of fine drops from the pen to the paper. This was accomplished by electrifying the ink-bottle and ink by a local electrical machine, and keeping the paper in contact with an uninsulated metal roller. Electric attraction between the electrified ink and the unelectrified paper thus drew the ink-drops out, and the pen, which never touched the paper, was quite unretarded by friction. Both these instruments had the inestimable advantage that the to and fro motions of the spot of light or the pen took place independently of ordinary earth-currents through the cable.

The arrangement of magnet and suspended coil in this instrument has become widely known as that of the " d'Arsonval galvanometer." This application was anticipated by Thomson, and is distinctly mentioned in his recorder patent, long before such galvanometers were ever used. It was later proposed by several experimenters before M. d'Arsonval.

It is not too much to say that, by his discussion of the speed of signalling, his services as an electrical engineer, and especially by his invention of instruments capable of responding to very feeble currents, Thomson made submarine telegraphy commercially possible. Later he entered into partnership with Mr. C. F. Varley and Professor Fleeming Jenkin. A combination of inventions was made by the firm : Varley had patented a method of signalling by condensers, and Jenkin later suggested and patented an automatic key for "curb-sending" on a cable—that is, signalling by placing one pole of the battery for an interval a little shorter than the usual one to the line, and then reversing the battery for the remainder. This gave sharper signals, as the reversal helped to discharge the cable more rapidly than it would have been by the mere connection to earth between two signals. The firm of Thomson, Varley & Jenkin took a prominent part in cable work ; and Thomson and Jenkin acted as engineers for many large undertakings. They employed a staff of young electricians at the cable-works at Millwall and elsewhere, keeping watch over the cable during manufacture, and sent them to sea as representatives and assistants to perform similar duties during the process of cable-laying. On their staff were many men who have come to eminence in electrical and engineering pursuits in later life.

Mariners' Compass and Sounding Machine

After the earlier Atlantic expeditions Sir William Thomson turned his attention to the construction of navigational instruments, and invented the mariner's compass and wire-sounding apparatus which are now so well known. He had come to the conclusion that the compasses in use had much too large needles (some of them bar-magnets seven or eight inches long !) to respond quickly and certainly to changes of course, and, what was still more serious, to admit of the application of correcting magnets, and of masses of soft-iron to annul the action of the magnetism of the ship.

The compass card consists of a paper ring, on which the "points" and degrees are engraved in the ordinary way, and is kept circular by a light ring of aluminium. Threads of silk extend radially from the rim to a central boss of aluminium in which is a cap of aluminium. In the top of the cap is a sapphire bearing, which rests on an iridium point projecting upward from the compass bowl. Eight magnets of glass-hard steel, from $3\frac{1}{4}$ inches to 2 inches long, and about the thickness of a knitting-needle, which form the compass needle, are strung like the steps of a rope ladder, on two silk threads attached to four of the radial threads.

The weight of the card is extremely small—only $170\frac{1}{2}$ grains; that is less than $\frac{2}{5}$ of an ounce. But the matter is not merely made small in amount ; it is distributed on the whole at a great distance from the axis ; consequently the period of free vibration is long, and the card is very steady. The great lightness of the card also causes the error due to friction on the point of support to be very small.

The errors of the compass in an iron ship are mainly the semicircular error and the quadrantal error. We can only briefly indicate how these arise and how they are corrected. The ship's magnetism may be considered as partly permanent, and partly inductive. The former changes only very slowly, the latter alters as the ship changes course and position. For the ship is a combination of longitudinal, transverse, and vertical girders and beams. As a whole it is a great iron or steel girder, but its structure gives it longitudinal, transverse, and vertical magnetisation. This disturbs the compass, which is also affected by the magnetisation of the iron or steel masts and spars, or of iron or steel carried as cargo.

The semicircular error is due to a great extent to permanent magnetism, but also in part to induced magnetism. It is so called because when the ship's head is turned through 360°, the error attains a maximum on two courses 180° apart. It may amount to over 20° in an ordinary iron vessel, and to 30° or 40° in an armour-clad. It is corrected by two sets of steel magnets placed with their centres under the needle in the binnacle. One set have their lengths fore and aft, the others in the thwart-ship direction. These magnets annul the error on the north and south and on the east and west courses, due to the two horizontal components of magnetic force produced mainly by the permanent magnetism of the ship. A regular routine of swinging the ship when marks on the shore (the true bearings of which from the ship are known) are available, is followed for the adjustment.

The quadrantal error is so called because its maxima are found on four compass courses successively a quadrant, or 90°, from one another. It amounts in general to from 5° to 10° at most. It is due to induced magnetism, and is corrected by a pair of soft-iron spheres, placed on the two sides of the compass with their centres in a line transverse to the ship, through the centre of the compass needle. There are, however, exceptional cases in which they are placed in the fore and aft line one afore, the other abaft, the needle. When the quadrantal error has once been annulled it is always zero, for as the induced magnetism changes, so does that of the spheres, and the adjustment remains good. In a new ship the permanent magnetism slowly alters, and so the semicircular correction has to be improved from time to time by changing the magnets.

These adjustments are not quite all that have to be made ; but enough has been stated to show how the process of compensation can be carried out with the Thomson compass. The immensely-too-large magnets used formerly as compass needles, through a mistaken notion, apparently, that more directive force would be got by their means, rendered the quadrantal adjustment an impossibility. The card swinging round brought the large needles into different positions relatively to the iron balls, when these were used, and exerted an inductive action on them which reacted on the needles, producing more error, perhaps, than was corrected.

Thomson invented also an instrument called a "deflector," by which it is possible to adjust a compass when sights of sun or stars, or bearings of terrestrial objects, cannot be obtained. By means of it the directive forces on the needles on different courses can be compared. Then the adjustment is made by placing the correctors so that the directive force is as nearly as may be the same on all courses. The compass is then quite correct.

The theory of deviations of the compass, it is right to say, was discussed first partially by Poisson, but afterwards very completely and elegantly by the late Mr. Archibald Smith of Jordanhill, whose memoirs, now incorporated in the *Admiralty Manual of Deviations of the Compass*, led to Lord Kelvin's inventions.

Lord Kelvin's compass is now almost universally in use in the merchant service of this country, and in most of the navies of the world. It has added greatly to the certainty and safety of navigation.

The sounding machine is also well known. At first pianoforte wire was used for deep-sea sounding by Commodore Belknap of the U.S. Navy, and by others, on Sir William Thomson's recommendation. Finally, a form of machine was made by which a sinker could be lowered to the bottom of the sea and brought up again in a few minutes; so that it was possible to take a sounding without the long delay involved in the old method with a reel of hemp-rope, which often tempted shipmasters to run risks of going ashore rather than stop the ship for the purpose. The wire offered little resistance to motion through the water, and by a proper winding machine, with brake to prevent the wire from running out too fast and kinking, when it was almost certain to break, one man could quickly sound and heave up again, while another attended to the wire and sinker. A gauge consisting of a long quill-tube closed at the upper end, and coated inside with chromate of silver, showed by the action of the sea-water on the coating how far the water had passed up the tube, compressing the air above it; and from this, by placing the tube along a wooden rule properly graduated, the depth was read off at once. With the improved machine a ship approaching the shore in thick weather could take soundings at short intervals without stopping, and discover at once any beginning of shallowing of the water, and so avoid danger.

The single wire is not now used, as a thin stranded wire is found safer and quite as effective. The gauge also has been improved. The apparatus can be seen in any well-found sea-going vessel; though there are still, or were until not very long ago, steam vessels without this apparatus, though crossing the English Channel with passengers. These depended for soundings on the obsolete hemp-rope, wrapped round an iron spindle held vertically on the deck by members of the ship's company, while the cord was unwound by the descent of the sinker.[1]

Sir William Thomson's electrical and other inventions are too numerous to specify here, and they are in constant use wherever precision of measurement is aimed at or required. Long ago he invented electrometers for absolute measurements of electrical potential ("electric pressure"); more recently his current-balances have given the same precision to electrodynamic measurement of currents. All his early instruments were made by Mr. James White, Glasgow. The

---

[1] The writer once, on a thick night, in a passenger steamer in the Race of Alderney, when the engines were stopped and soundings were being taken, saw the reel and cord go overboard, nearly taking one of the men with it. A new hank of cord had to be got and bent on a new reel; an operation that took a long time, during which the exact locality of the ship was a matter of uncertainty. Comment is needless!

business founded by Mr. White, and latterly carried on at Cambridge Street, has developed immensely, and is now owned by a limited liability company—Messrs. Kelvin and James White (Limited).

For many years Sir William Thomson was a keen yachtsman, and his schooner yacht, the *Lalla Rookh*, was well known on the Clyde and in the Solent. An expert navigator, he delighted to take deep-sea voyages in his yacht, and went more than once as far as Madeira. Many navigational and hydrodynamical problems were worked out on these expeditions. For a good many years, however, he had given up seafaring during his times of relaxation, and lived in Glasgow and London and in Largs, Ayrshire, where he built, in 1875, a large and comfortable house, looking out towards the Firth and the Argyleshire lochs he knew and loved so well.

In the course of his deep-sea expeditions in his yacht he became impressed with the utility of Sumner's method of determining the position of a ship. Let us suppose that at a given instant the altitude of the sun is determined from the ship. The Greenwich mean-time, and therefore the longitude at which the sun is vertical, is known by chronometer, and the declination of the sun is known from the Nautical Almanac. The point on the earth vertically under the sun can be marked on the chart, and a circle (or rather, what would be a circle on a terrestrial globe) drawn round it from every point of which the sun would have the observed altitude. The ship is at a point on this circle. Some time after the altitude of the sun is observed again, and a new " circle " is drawn. If the first " circle " be bodily shifted on the chart along the

distance run in the interval, it will intersect the second
in two points, one of which will be the position of the
ship, and it is generally possible to tell which, without
danger of mistake.

Sir William Thomson printed tables for facilitating
the calculations in the use of Sumner's method, and continually used them in his own voyages. He was well
versed in seamanship of all kinds, and used his experience
habitually to throw light on abstruse problems of
dynamics. Some of these will be found in " Thomson
and Tait"; for instance, in Part I, § 325, where a
number of nautical phenomena are cited in illustration
of an important principle of hydrodynamics. The fifth
example stated is as follows : "In a smooth sea, with
moderate wind blowing parallel to the shore, a sailing
ship heading towards the shore, with not enough of
sail set, can only be saved from creeping ashore by
setting more sail, and sailing rapidly towards the shore,
or the danger that is to be avoided, so as to allow her
to be steered away from it. The risk of going ashore
in fulfilment of Lagrange's equations is a frequent
incident of 'getting under way' while lifting anchor
or even after slipping from moorings." His seamanship was well known to ship-masters, with whom he
had much intercourse, and whose intelligence and
practical skill he held in very high regard.

CHAPTER XVI

LORD KELVIN IN HIS CLASS-ROOM AND LABORATORY

It is impossible to convey to those who never studied at Glasgow any clear conception of Thomson as he appeared to students whom he met daily during the session. His appearance at meetings of the British Association, and his vivacious questionings of the various authors of papers, his absorption in his subject and oblivion to the flight of time when he read a paper, himself, will long be remembered by scientific men : but though they suffice to suggest what he was like in his own lecture-room, the picture lacks the setting of furniture, apparatus, assistants, and students, which all contributed to the unique impression made by his personality on his pupils. The lecture-table— with long straight front and ends refracted inward, flanked by higher small round tables supported on cylindrical pillars—laden with instruments ; the painted diagrams of the solar spectrum and of the paths of coloured rays through a prism, hung round the walls ; the long wire with the cylindrical vibrator attached, for experiments on torsion, and the triple spiral spring vibrator, which hung at the two ends of the long black-board ; the pendulum thirty feet long, consisting of a steel wire and a twelve-pound cannon-ball as bob, suspended from the apex of the dome-roof above the lecture-table ; the large iron wheel in the beautiful

oriel window on the right of the lecturer, and the
collection of optical instruments on the table in front
of the central window spaces, from which the small
iron-framed panes—dear to the heart of the architect
—had been removed ; the clock on either side of the
room, one motionless, the other indicating the time,
and having attached to it the alarm which showed
when the " angry bell " outside had ceased to toll ; the
ten benches of eager and merry students, which filled
the auditorium ; all these combined to form a scene
which every student fondly recalls, and which cannot
be adequately described.   A similar scene, with some
differences of arrangement and having its own particular
associations, will occur to every student who attended
in the Old College.

The writer will never forget the lecture-room when
he first beheld it, from his place on Bench VIII, a few
days after the beginning of session 1874–5.   Sir
William Thomson, with activity emphasised rather
than otherwise by his lameness, came in with the
students, passed behind the table, and, putting up
his eye-glass, surveyed the apparatus set out.   Then,
as the students poured in, an increasing stream, the
alarm weight was released by the bell-ringer, and fell
slowly some four or five feet, from the top of the clock
to a platform below.   By the time the weight had
descended the students were in their places, and then,
as Thomson advanced to the table, all rose to their
feet, and he recited the third Collect from the Morning Service of the Church of England.   It was the
custom then, and it is still one better honoured in
the observance than in the breach (which has become
rather common) to open all the first and second classes

of the day with prayer; and the selection of the prayers was left to the discretion of the professors. Next came the roll-call by the assistant; each name was called in its English, or Scottish (for the clans were always well represented) form, and the answer "adsum" was returned.

Then the Professor began his lecture, generally with the examination of one of the students, who rose in his place when his name was called. Thomson, as the quotation in Chapter VI from the Bangor Address shows, was fond of oral examination, and after the second hour had begun to decline as one of regular attendance, habitually devoted ten or fifteen minutes to asking questions and criticising the answers. The names of the students to be questioned were selected at random from the class register, or by a kind of lottery, carried out by placing a small card for each student in a box on the table, and drawing a name whenever a member of the class was to be examined. The interest in the drawing each day was intense, for there was a glorious uncertainty as to what might be the line of examination adopted. Sometimes, in the midst of a criticism of an answer, an idea would suddenly occur to the Professor, and he would enlarge upon it, until the forgotten examinee slipped quietly back into his seat, to be no more disturbed at least for that day! And how great the relief if the ordeal was well passed and the card was placed in that receptacle of the blessed, the compartment reserved for those who had been called and duly passed the assize! But there was a third compartment reserved for the cards of those unfortunates who failed to satisfy the judge! The reader may have anticipated the fact that the three divisions of this fateful box were commonly known to students by the names of the three great habitations of spirits described in the *Divina Commedia* of Dante.

As has been stated, the oral examination with which the lectures opened was the cause of a good deal of excitement, which was added to by the element of chance introduced by drawing the names from the purgatorial compartment of the box. The ordeal was dreaded by backward students, whom Thomson found, as he said, aphasic, when called on to answer in examination, but who certainly were anything but aphasic in more congenial circumstances. Occasionally they abstained from responding to their names, modestly seeking the seclusion of the crowd, and some little time would be spent in ascertaining whether the examinee-designate was present. When at last he was discovered, he generally rose with a fervent appeal to his fellows on either side to help him in his need.

McFarlane used to tell of an incident which illustrated the ingenuity with which it was sometimes attempted to evade the ordeal of the *viva voce* examination. One afternoon, when he was busily preparing the lecture-illustrations for next day, a student came into the class-room, and engaging him in conversation on some point of dynamics, regarding which he professed to have a difficulty, hovered round the box which contained the three compartments popularly known as Purgatory, Heaven, and Hell ! Always when McFarlane left the room to bring something from the adjoining cabinet of apparatus, he found, when he returned, his inquiring friend hurriedly quitting the immediate vicinity of the box. At last the student took leave, with many apologies for giving so much trouble. As McFarlane suspected would be the case, the ticket bearing the name of that student was no longer to be found ! He used to conclude the story as follows : " I just made a new ticket for him, and placed it on the top of the other tickets, and next day Sir William called him, the very first time." What were his feelings, who had fondly thought himself safe for the session, and now found himself subjected to a " heckling " which he probably expected would be repeated indefinitely, may be imagined.

The subject of the first lecture which the writer attended was simple harmonic motion, and was illustrated by means of pendulums, spiral springs with weights, a long vertical rod of steel tipped with an ivory ball and fastened to a heavy base, tuning-forks, etc.

The motion was defined as that of a particle moving along the diameter of a circle—the " auxiliary circle," Thomson called it—so as always to keep pace, as regards displacement in the direction along that diameter, with a particle moving with uniform speed in the circle. Then the velocity and acceleration were found, and it was shown that the particle was continually accelerated towards the centre in proportion to the distance of the particle from that point. The constant ratio of acceleration to displacement was proved to be equal to the square of the angular velocity in the auxiliary circle, and from this fact, and the particular value of the acceleration when the particle was at either end of its range of motion, an expression for the period in terms of the speed and radius of the auxiliary circle was deduced.   Then the ordinary simple pendulum formula was obtained.

This mode of treatment of an elementary matter, so
entirely different from anything in the ordinary text-
books, arrested the attention at once, and conveyed, to
some at least of those present, an idea of simple harmonic motion which was directly applicable to all kinds
of cases, such as the motion of the air in a sound wave,
or of the medium which conveys the waves of light.

The subject of Kepler's laws was dealt with in the
early lectures of every course, and Newton's deductions
were insisted on as containing the philosophy of the
whole question, leading, as they did, to the single
principle from which the laws could be deduced, and
the third law corrected when the mass of the planet
was comparable with that of the sun. Sometimes
Thomson would read the remarkable passage in
Hegel's *Logik*, in which he refers to the Newtonian
theory of gravitation and says, " The planets are not
pulled this way and that, they move along in their
orbits like the blessed gods," and remark upon it.
On one occasion his remark was, " Well, gentlemen,
if these be his physics, what must his metaphysics be ? "
And certainly that a *philosopher* should deny, as Hegel
seemed to do, all merit to the philosophical setting in
which Newton placed the empirical results of Kepler,
is a very remarkable phenomenon.

The vivacity and enthusiasm of the Professor at that
time were very great. The animation of his counten-
ance as he looked at a gyrostat spinning, standing on a
knife-edge on the glass plate in front of him, and
leaning over so that its centre of gravity was on one
side of the point of support ; the delight with which he
showed that hurrying of the precessional motion caused
the gyrostat to rise, and retarding the precessional

motion caused the gyrostat to fall, so that the freedom
to "precess" was the secret of its not falling; the
immediate application of the study of the gyrostat to
the explanation of the precession of the equinoxes, and
illustration by a model of a terrestrial globe, arranged so
that the centre should be a fixed point, while its axis—
a material spike of brass—rolled round a horizontal
circle, the centre of which represented the pole of the
ecliptic, and the diameter of which subtended an angle
at the centre of the globe of twice the obliquity of the
ecliptic; the pleasure with which he pointed to the
motion of the equinoctial points along a circle surrounding the globe on a level with its centre, and
representing the plane of the ecliptic, and the smile
with which he announced, when the axis had rolled
once round the circle, that 26,000 years had elapsed—
all these delighted his hearers, and made the lecture
memorable.

Then the gyrostat, mounted with its axis vertical on
trunnions on a level with the fly-wheel, and resting on
a wooden frame carried about by the professor! The
delight of the students with the quiescence of the
gyrostat when the frame, gyrostat and all, was carried
round in the direction of the spin of the fly-wheel, and
its sudden turning upside down when the frame was
carried round the other way, was extreme, and when
he suggested that a gyrostat might be concealed on a
tray of glasses carried by a waiter, their appreciation
of what would happen was shown by laughter and a
tumult of applause.

Some would have liked to follow the motions of
spinning bodies a little more closely, and to have made
out clearly why they behaved as they did. Apparently

Thomson imagined the whole affair was self-evident, for he never gave more than the simple parallelogram diagram showing the composition, with the already existing angular momentum about the axis of the top, of that generated about another axis, in any short time, by the action of gravity.

As a matter of fact, the stability and instability of the gyrostat on the tray give the best possible illustration of the two different forms of solution of the differential equation, $\ddot{\theta} + \mu\theta = 0$, according as μ is positive or negative; though it is also possible to explain the inversion very simply from first principles. All this was no doubt regarded by Thomson as obvious; but it was far from being self-evident to even good students of the ordinary class, who, without exception, were beginning the study of dynamics.

Thomson's absorption in the work of the moment was often very great, and on these occasions he much disliked to be brought down to sublunary things by any slight mischance or inconvenience. Examples will occur to every old pupil of the great emphasis with which he commanded that precautions should be taken to prevent the like from happening again. Copies of Thomson and Tait's *Natural Philosophy*—" T and T' " was its familiar title—and of other books, including Barlow's Tables and other collections of numerical data, were always kept on the lecture-table. But occasionally a laboratory student would stray in after everything had been prepared for the morning lecture, and carry off *Barlow* to make some calculation, and of course forget to return it. Next morning some number would be wanted from *Barlow* in a hurry, and the book would be missing. Then Thomson would order that *Barlow* should be chained to the lecture-table, and enjoin his assistant to see that that was done without an hour's delay!

On one occasion, after working out part of a calculation on the long fixed blackboard on the wall behind the table, his chalk gave out, and he dropped his hand down to the long ledge which projected from the bottom of the board to find another piece. None was just there; and he had to walk a step or two to obtain one. So he enjoined McFarlane, his assistant, who was always in attendance, to have a sufficient number of pieces on the ledge in future, to enable him to find one handy wherever he might need it. McFarlane forgot the injunction, or could not obtain more chalk at the time, and the same thing happened next day. So the command was issued, " McFarlane, I told you to get plenty of chalk, and you haven't done it. Now have a *hundred* pieces of chalk on this ledge to-morrow; remember, a *hundred* pieces; I will count them!" McFarlane, afraid to be caught napping again, sent that afternoon for several boxes of chalk, and carefully laid the new shining white sticks on the shelf, all neatly parallel at an angle to the edge. The shelf was about sixteen feet long, so that there was one piece of chalk for every two inches, and the effect was very fine. The class next morning was delighted, and very appreciative of McFarlane's diligence. Thomson came in, put up his eye-glass, looked at the display, smiled sweetly, and, turning to the applauding students, began his lecture.

From time to time there were special experiments, which excited the interest of the class to an extraordinary degree. One was the determination of the velocity of a bullet fired from a rifle into a Robins ballistic pendulum. The pendulum, consisting of a massive bob of lead attached to a rigid frame of iron bars turning about knife-edges, was set up behind the lecture-table, and the bullet was fired by Thomson from a Jacob rifle into the bob of the pendulum. The velocity was deduced from the deflection of the pendulum, its known moment of inertia about the line of the knife-edges, the distance of the line of fire from that line, and the mass of the bullet.

In some of the notices of Lord Kelvin that have appeared in the newspapers, the imagination of the writers has converted the Jacob rifle into one which Professor Thomson carried in the early years of the volunteer movement, as a member of a Glasgow corps. It is still used in the Natural Philosophy Department for the same experiment, and is a muzzle-loading rifle of large calibre, which throws an ounce bullet. It was invented by the well-known Indian sportsman, Colonel Jacob, for big-game shooting in India. Thomson held a commission as captain in the K (or University) Company of rifle volunteers, and so did not shoulder a rifle, except when he may have indulged in target practice.

The front bench students were always in a state of excitement, mingled in some cases perhaps with a little trepidation. For the target was very near them, and though danger was averted by placing a large wooden screen in front of the bob, to prevent splinters of the bullet from flying about in the event of its missing the target and striking the iron casing of the bob, there was a slight amount of nervousness as to what might happen. The rifle, loaded by McFarlane, who had weighed out the charge of powder (so many drams) from a prescription kept in a cavity of the stock, was placed on the table, and two rests, provided with $\bigvee$ notches to receive the rifle, were placed in the proper position to enable a bull's eye to be obtained. Thomson generally produced a small box of cotton wool, and inserted a little in each of his ears to prevent injury to the tympanum from the report, and advised the spectators to do the same. Then, adjusting his eye-glass, he bent down, placed the rifle in position, and fired, and the solemn stillness with which the aiming and adjustments had been witnessed was succeeded by vociferous applause. The length of tape drawn out under a light spring was read off by McFarlane, who had already placed on the blackboard the formula for calculation of the velocity, with the factor by which the length of tape had to be multiplied to give the velocity in feet per second. Then, with the intimation that a question involving numerical calculation would be set on the subject, in the ensuing Monday morning examination paper, the lecture generally closed, or was rounded off with some further observations on angular (or, as Thomson always preferred to call it, moment of) momentum.

Long after in the course of a debate in the House of Lords on a proposal to make the use of the metric system of weights and measures compulsory, Lord Kelvin told their lordships how he had weighed out the powder to charge this rifle, and, mistaking the weights, had loaded the rifle with an amount of powder which would have been almost certain to burst the piece, but had happily paused before firing it off.

He often interrupted the course of a lecture with a

denunciation of the British "no-system of weights and measures"—"insane," "brain-wasting," dangerous," were among the mildest epithets he applied to it, and he would deeply sympathise with the student whose recollection of avoirdupois weight, troy weight, apothecaries' weight, etc., was somewhat hazy. The danger of the system consisted mainly in the fact that the apothecaries' dram is 60 grains, while the avoirdupois dram is $27\frac{1}{3}$ grains. Thus so many drams of powder required to charge a rifle is a very much larger quantity when reckoned in apothecaries' drams than when reckoned in avoirdupois. As a rule he left the loading of the rifle, like all the other lecture-room experiments, to his assistants.

Another experiment which caused a great sensation was that known as the "dew-drop"! A funnel of brass, composed of a tube about 30 inches long and an inch wide, and a conical mouth about ten inches wide, had a piece of stout sheet India-rubber stretched, as tightly as it could be by hand, across its mouth, and made water-tight by a serving of twine and cement round the edge. A wire soldered round the outside of the lip gave a good hold for this serving and made all perfectly secure. On the plane surface of the sheet geometrical figures were drawn in ink, so that their distortion could be afterwards studied. The funnel was then hung by a strong support in an inverted position behind the table, and water poured gently into it from a rubber supply pipe connected with the water-main. As the water was allowed to accumulate —very slowly at first—the sheet of rubber gradually stretched and bulged out, at first to a flat lens-shape, and gradually more and more, till an immense water-drop had been formed, 15 or 18 inches in horizontal diameter, and of still greater vertical dimensions. The rubber film was now, at the place of greatest tension, quite thin and transparent, and its giving way was anticipated by the students with keen enjoyment. A large tub had been placed below to receive the water, but the deluge always extended over the whole floor space behind the table, and was greeted with rapturous applause.

Before the drop burst, and while it was forming, Thomson discoursed on surface tension, emphasising the essential difference between the tension in the rubber-film and the surface-film of a dewdrop, and pointing out how the geometrical figures had changed in shape. Then he would poke it with the pointer he held in his hand, and, turning to the class, as the mass quivered, remark, " The trembling of the dewdrop, gentlemen ! "

Vibrations of elastic solids were illustrated in various ways, frequently by means of a symmetrical shape of calves'-foot jelly, at the top of which a coloured marble had been imbedded as a molecule, the motions of which could be followed. And then he would discourse on the Poisson-Navier theory of isotropic solids, and the impossibility of the fixed relation which that theory imposed between the modulus of rigidity and the modulus of compression ; and refer with approval to the series of examples of " perfectly uniform, homogeneous, isotropic solids," which Stokes had shown could be obtained by making jellies of different degrees of stiffness. Another example, frequently adduced as indicating the falsity of the theory, was the entirely different behaviour of blocks of India-rubber and cork, under compression applied by a Bramah press. The cork diminished in thickness without spreading out laterally ; the rubber, being very little compressible, bulged out all round as its thickness was diminished.

The lectures on acoustics, which came late in the course, were also exceedingly popular. Two French horns, with all their crooks and accessories, were displayed, and sometimes, to the great delight of the class, Thomson would essay to show how the pitch of a note could be modified by means of the keys, or by the hand inserted in the bell. The determination by the siren of the pitch of the notes of tuning-forks excited by a 'cello bow, and the tuning of a major third by sounding at the same time the perfect fifth of the lower note, were often exhibited, and commented on with acute remarks, of which it is a pity no statement was ever published.[1]

The closing lecture of the ordinary course was usually on light, and the subject which was generally the last to be taken up—for as the days lengthened in spring, it was possible sometimes to obtain sunlight for the experiments—was often relegated to the last day or two of the session. So after an hour's lecture Thomson would say, " As this is the last day of the session, I will go on for a little longer, after those who have to leave have gone to their classes." Then he would resume after ten o'clock, and go on to eleven, when another opportunity would be given for students to leave, and the lecture would be again resumed. Messengers would

[1] The tuning of a major third, in this way, is described in the paper entitled " Beats on Imperfect Harmonies," published in *Popular Lectures and Addresses*, vol. ii.

be sent from his house, where he was wanted for business of different sorts, to find out what had become of him, and the answer brought would be, hour after hour, " He is still lecturing." At last he would conclude about one o'clock, and gently thank the small and devoted band who had remained to the end, for their kind and prolonged attention.

In the course of his lectures Thomson continually called on his assistants for data of all kinds. In the busiest time of his life—the fifteen years from 1870 to 1885—he trusted to his assistants for the preparation of his class illustrations, and it was sometimes a little difficult to anticipate his wishes, for without careful rehearsal it is almost impossible to make sure that in an experimental lecture everything will go without a hitch. The digressions, generally most interesting and instructive, in which he frequently indulged, almost always rendered it necessary to bring some experiment before the class which had not been anticipated, and all kinds of things were kept in readiness, lest they should be wanted suddenly.

It has often been asserted that Thomson appealed to his assistant for information contained in the multiplication-table, and could not perform the ordinary operations of arithmetic. His active mind, working on ahead of the statements he was making at the moment, often could not be brought back to the consideration of the value of 9 times 6, and the like ; but it was quite untrue that he was incapable of making calculations. His memory was good, and though he never could be, for example, sure whether the aqueous humour was before or behind the crystalline in the eye, he was generally able at once to tell when a misstatement had been made as to any numerical question regarding the subject under discussion.

In the higher mathematical class, to which he lectured on Wednesdays, at noon, Thomson was exceedingly interesting. There he seemed to work at the subject as he lectured ; new points to be investigated continually presented themselves, and the students were encouraged to work them out in the week-long intervals between his lectures. Always the physical interpretation of results was aimed at, even intermediate steps were discussed. Thus the meaning of the mathematical processes was ever kept in view, and the men who could follow were made to think while they worked, and to regard the mathematical analysis as merely an aid, not an end in itself. " A little expenditure of chalk is a saving of brains ; " " the art of reading mathematical books is judicious skipping," were remarks he sometimes made, and illustrate his view of the relative importance of mathematical work when he regarded it as the handmaid of the physical thinker. Yet he valued mathematics for its own sake, and was keenly alive to elegance of form and method, as readers of such great mathematical discussions as the " Appendix on Spherical Harmonics," in Thomson and Tait, will observe. He spoke with unqualified admiration of the work of Green and Stokes, of Cauchy's great memoir on Waves, and of Hamilton's papers on Dynamics. But no form of vector-analysis, neither the Quaternions of Hamilton nor the Vectors of Willard Gibbs and Heaviside, appealed to him, and the example of his friend and co-worker, Tait, had no effect in modifying his adverse verdict regarding this department of mathematics,

a verdict which in later years became only more
emphatic.

One session he began the first lecture of the higher
class by writing $\frac{dx}{dt}$ in the middle of the blackboard,
and demanding of each of the ten or a dozen students
present, some of them distinguished graduates, what it
meant !   One student described it as the limiting value
of the ratio of the increment of the dependent variable
x to the increment of the independent variable t, when
the latter increment is made indefinitely small.   He
retorted, " That's what Todhunter would say ! "   The
others gave various slightly different versions of the same
definition.   At last he impatiently remarked, " Does
nobody know that dx/dt means velocity ? "   Here
the physical idea as a whole was before his mind ; and
he did not reflect that if t denoted time and x distance
in any direction, the explanation given by the student
did describe velocity with fair accuracy.

An embarrassing peculiarity of his mathematical
discussions was his tendency, when a difficulty of
symbolisation occurred, to completely change the
notation.   Also he was not uniformly accurate in
analytical work ; but he more than made up for this
by the faculty he had of devising a test of the accuracy
of the result and of divining the error which had crept
in, if the test was not satisfied.

The subjects he treated were always such great
branches of mathematics as the theory of the tides—
he discussed the tidal phenomena of the English
Channel in one course—the general theory of vibrations, Fourier analysis, the theory of waves in water,
etc., etc.   A very good idea of the manner and matter

of his mathematical prelections can be obtained from a perusal of the *Baltimore Lectures*.

In the physical laboratory he was both inspiring and distracting. He continually thought of new things to be tried, and interrupted the course of the work with interpolated experiments which often robbed the preceding sequence of operations of their final result. His ideas were on the whole better worked out by a really good corps of students when he was from home, and could only communicate by letter his views on the work set forth in the daily reports which were forwarded to him.

He insisted with emphasis that a student who found that a quadrant electrometer would not work well should take it to pieces to ascertain what was the matter. This of course generally resulted in the return of the instrument to White's shop to be put together again and adjusted. But, as he said, there was a cause for every trouble of that kind, and the great thing was to find out at once what it was.

Thomson's concentration on the work in hand, and his power of simply taking possession of men, even mere spectators, and converting them into assistants, was often shown in the laboratory. Several men who have since become eminent were among the assistants enrolled from the laboratory students. Professor W. E. Ayrton and, later, Professor John Perry, were students at Glasgow for a time, and rendered the most able and willing help in the researches which were then proceeding. This power was, no doubt, the secret of his success in gathering round him an enthusiastic corps of laboratory workers in the early years of his professorship, and it was shown also by the ease with which he annexed the Blackstone examination-room and, later, various spaces in the new University buildings. There, after a time, the Natural Philosophy rooms were found by the senatus to include not only the original class-room, laboratory, etc., but also all the spare attics and corridors in the neighbourhood, and even the University tower itself! One of his colleagues, who venerated him highly, remarked recently, "He had a great faculty for annexation!"

The incident referred to occurred while he was preparing the article on *Heat* for the ninth edition of the *Encyclopædia Britannica.* It seemed at first a pity that Thomson should undertake to write such articles; but in the course of their preparation he came upon so many points on which experimental information was wanting, and instituted so many researches to answer his questions, that the essays took very much the character of original papers. In the article on *Heat* (he also wrote *Elasticity*), will be found a long account of "Steam Thermometry," that is, of thermometers in which the indicating substance was to be the saturated vapours of different substances, water, sulphurous acid, etc., etc., for he did not limit the term "steam" to water-vapour. For some time every one in the laboratory was employed in making sulphurous acid, by heating copper in sulphuric acid in the usual way, and condensing the gas in tubes immersed in freezing mixtures; and the atmosphere of the room was of a sort which, however noxious to germs of different kinds, it was a little difficult to breathe. One morning, when all were thus occupied, an eminent chemist, who had just come home from the south for a vacation, called to pay his respects. After a word or two of inquiry as to how his young friend was prospering in his new post, Thomson said, " We are all very busy brewing liquid sulphurous acid, for use in sulphurous acid steam thermometers ; we want a large quantity of the liquid ; would you mind helping us ? " So, desiring an assistant to find a flask and materials, he enrolled this new and excellent recruit on the spot ; and what was intended to be a mere call, was prolonged into a long day of ungrudging work at an elementary chemical exercise !

CHAPTER XVII

PRACTICAL ACTIVITIES—HONOURS AND DISTINCTIONS
—LAST ILLNESS AND DEATH

It remains to say something of Lord Kelvin's public and practical activities. All over the world he came ultimately to be recognised as the greatest living scientific authority in almost all branches of physics. Every existing learned society sought to make him a Fellow, honorary degrees were showered on him from all quarters. A list of some of the most important of these distinctions is given in the Royal Society Year-Book for 1907 ; it is doubtful if a complete list could be compiled. He was awarded the Keith Medal and the Victoria Jubilee Medal by the Royal Society of Edinburgh, and received in succession the Copley and Royal Medals of the Royal Society of London, of which he was elected a Fellow in 1851, and was President from 1890 to 1895. For several periods of years he was President of the Royal Society of Edinburgh, to which he communicated his papers on heat, dissipation of energy, vortex motion, and many other memoirs.

He was President of the British Association at the Edinburgh meeting in 1871, when he delivered a presidential address, noteworthy in many respects, but chiefly remarkable in the popular mind on account of his suggestion that life was conveyed to the earth by a seed, a germ enclosed in a crevice of a meteorite. This was understood at the time by many people as an attempt to explain the origin of life itself, instead of what it was intended to be, an explanation of the beginning of the existence of living things on a planet which was originally, on the completion of its formation by the condensation of nebular matter, red hot even at its surface. On several occasions he was president of Section A, and he was constant in attendance at the Association meetings, and an eager listener and participator in the discussions and debates. His scientific curiosity was never at rest, and he dearly liked to meet and converse with scientific workers.

Lady Thomson, who had been long an invalid, died in 1870, and in 1874 Sir William Thomson was married to Miss Frances Anna Blandy (daughter of Mr. Charles R. Blandy of Madeira) who survives him as Lady Kelvin. To her tender solicitude he owed much of his constant and long-continued activity in all kinds of work. She accompanied him on all public occasions, and he relied greatly on her helpfulness and ever watchful care.

In 1892 Sir William Thomson, while President of the Royal Society, was raised to the Peerage, with the title of Baron Kelvin of Netherhall, Largs ; and more lately he was created a member of the Order of Merit and a G.C.V.O. His foreign distinctions were very numerous. He was a Knight of the Order *Pour le Mérite* of Prussia, a Foreign Associate of the Institute of France, and a Grand Officer of the Legion of Honour. But no public honour or mark of royal favour could raise him in the estimation of all who know anything of science or of the labours of the scientific men to whom we owe the necessities and luxuries of our present civilisation.

In 1896 the City and University of Glasgow celebrated the jubilee of his Professorship of Natural Philosophy. The rejoicings on that occasion will never be forgotten by those whose privilege it was to take part in them. Delegates came from every country in the world, and kings and princes, universities and learned societies, colleges and scholastic institutions of every kind, vied with each other in doing honour to the veteran who had fought for truth and light for so many years, and won so many victories. A memorial volume of the proceedings was published, including a review of Lord Kelvin's work by the late Professor FitzGerald, and a full report appeared in *Nature* and other journals at the time, so that it is unnecessary to give particulars here. And indeed it is impossible by any verbal description to convey an idea of the enthusiasm with which the scientific world acclaimed its leader, and of the dignity and state of the ceremonies.

In 1899, at the age of seventy-five, Lord Kelvin resigned the Chair of Natural Philosophy, and retired, not to rest, but to investigate more vigorously than ever the properties of matter. One remarkable fruit of his leisure we have in his great book, the *Baltimore Lectures*, in which theories of light are discussed with a power which excites the reverence of all engaged in the new researches and which recent discoveries have called into existence. And it is not too much to say that the means of discussing and extending these discoveries are in great measure due to Lord Kelvin.

During the year 1907 Lord Kelvin performed many University duties and seemed to be in unusually good health. He presided as Chancellor at the installation of Mr. Asquith as Lord Rector on January 11, and in the same capacity attended a few days later the funeral of Principal Story, the Vice-Chancellor, who died on January 13. On April 23 he presided at the long and arduous ceremonies of honorary graduation, and the public opening of the new Natural Philosophy Institute and the new Medical Buildings, by the Prince of Wales. As Chancellor he conferred the degree of Doctor of Laws on the Prince and Princess, and took the chair at the luncheon which followed the proceedings, when he proposed in a short and graceful speech the health of the Princess.

He was able to take part also in various political and social meetings, and to give attention to the work in progress at the factories of his firm in Cambridge Street. Lady Kelvin and he left Netherhall, Largs, for Aix les Bains, at the end of July, but visited the British Association at Leicester in passing. There he heard the presidential address of his old friend, Sir David Gill, to whom he moved a vote of thanks in his usual vivacious manner.

Lord Kelvin had been accustomed for a good many years to spend a month or six weeks in summer or early autumn at the famous French watering-place, from which he seemed always to receive much benefit. For a long time he had suffered from an intermittent and painful form of facial neuralgia, which, except during its attacks, which came and passed suddenly, did not incapacitate him from work. With the exception of a rather serious illness in 1906, this was the only ailment from which he had suffered for many years, and his general health was otherwise uniformly good.

Lord and Lady Kelvin returned to Netherhall on September 14, with the intention of going in a day or two to Belfast, to open the new scientific buildings of Queen's College. But, unfortunately, on the day of their arrival Lady Kelvin became very seriously ill, and the visit to Ireland had to be abandoned. His address was, however, read by his nephew, James Thomson, son of his elder brother, and was a tribute to the city of his birth, and the memory of his father.

The illness of Lady Kelvin caused much anxiety for many weeks, and this, and perhaps some incautious exposure, led to the impairment of Lord Kelvin's health. A chill caught on November 23 caused him to be confined to bed ; and though he managed for a week or two still to do some work on a paper with which he had been occupied for a considerable time, he became worse, and gradually sank, until his death at a quarter-past ten o'clock on the evening of December 18.

The keen sorrow which was universally felt for Lord Kelvin's death was manifested by all classes of the community. In Glasgow every one mourned as for the greatest of the land, and the testimony to the affection in which he was held, and the reverence for his character and scientific achievements, was extraordinary. And this feeling was universal ; from all parts of the world poured in telegrams of respectful sympathy with Lady Kelvin and with the University of Glasgow in their bereavement.

The view was immediately and strongly expressed, both privately and by the press, that the most illustrious natural philosopher since Newton should rest beside the great founder of physical science in Westminster

Abbey, and a requisition was immediately prepared and forwarded by the Royal Society of London to the Dean of Westminster. The wish of the whole scientific world was at once acceded to, and on December 23, at noon, the interment took place, with a state and yet a simplicity which will never be forgotten by those who were present.

Nearly all the scientific notabilities of the country were present, and the coffin, preceded by the choristers and the clergy, while the hymn, " Brief life is here our portion," was sung, was followed round the cloistered aisles from St. Faith's chapel to the choir, by the relatives, representatives of His Majesty the King and the Prince of Wales, by the Royal Society, by delegates from the Institute of France, representatives of the Universities of Cambridge, Oxford, Glasgow, and other universities, of the Royal Society of Edinburgh (of which Lord Kelvin was president when he died), and of most of the learned societies of the kingdom. Then, after a short service, the body was followed to the grave in the cloisters by the same company of mourners, and to the solemn words of the Burial Service was laid close by where rests all that was mortal of Isaac Newton. There he sleeps well who toiled during a long life for the cause of natural knowledge, and served nobly, as a hero of peace, his country and the world.

CONCLUSION

THE imperfect sketch of Lord Kelvin's scientific life and work which this book contains can only give a faint notion of the great achievements of the long life that has now ended. Beyond the researches which he carried out and the discoveries he made, there is the inspiration which his work and example gave to others. Inspired himself by Lagrange, Laplace, Ampère, and Fourier, and led to experimental research by the necessity for answers to the questions which his mathematical expression of the discoveries of the twenty-five years which preceded the establishment of his laboratory had suggested—the theories of electricity and magnetism, of heat, of elasticity, his discoveries in general dynamics and in fluid motion, the publication of " Thomson and Tait," all made him the inspirer of others ; and there was no one, however eminent, who was not proud to acknowledge his obligations to his genius. Clerk Maxwell, before he wrote the most original treatise on electricity that has ever appeared, gave himself to the study of Faraday's Experimental Researches and to the papers of Thomson. And if some, like FitzGerald and others, have regretted that the electromagnetic theory of light to which Maxwell was led by Faraday, and, indeed, by Thomson himself, did not meet with a more sympathetic reception at his hands, they have not been unmindful of the source from which much of their illumination has come.

He has founded a school of thought in mathematical physics, of men in whose minds the symbol is always the servant of the ideas, whose motto is interpretation by dynamical processes and models as far as that is possible, who shirk no mathematical difficulties when they have to be encountered, but are never led away from the straight road to the goal which they seek to reach—the systematic and clear formulation of the course of physical action.

And in Lord Kelvin's mind there was blended with a clear physical instinct which put aside all that was extraneous and unessential to the main issue an extraordinary power of concentration on the problem in hand, and a determination that was never daunted by failure, which consented to postponement but never to relinquishment, and which led often after long intervals of time to success in the end.   He believed that light would come at last on the most baffling of problems, if only it were looked at from every point of view and its conditions were completely formulated ; but he could put what was for the time impossible aside, and devote himself to the immediately possible and realisable.   And as often happens with every thinker, his mind, released from the task, returned to it of itself, and what before appeared shrouded in impenetrable mist stood out suddenly sharp and distinct like a mountain-top before a climber who has at last risen above the clouds.

With the great mathematical power and sure instinct which led him to success in physical research was combined a keen perception of the importance of practical applications.   Sometimes the practical question suggested the theoretical and experimental research, as when the needs of submarine telegraphy led to the discussion of the speed of signalling and the evolution of the reflecting galvanometer and the siphon recorder. On the other hand, the mathematical theory of electricity and magnetism had led to quantitative measurement and absolute units at an earlier time, when the need for these was beginning to be felt clearly by scientific workers and dimly by those far-sighted practical men who dreamed— for a dream it was thought at the time—of linking the Old World with the New by a submarine cable. But the quantitative study of electricity in the laboratory threw light on economic conditions, and the mass of data already obtained, mainly as a mere matter of experimental investigation of the properties of matter, became at once a valuable asset of the race of submarine cable engineers which suddenly sprang into existence.

And so it has been with the more recent applications of electricity. The induction of currents discovered by Faraday could not become of practical importance until its laws had been quantitatively discussed, a much longer process than that of discovery ; and we have seen how the British Association Committee, led by Thomson and Maxwell, brought the ideas and quantities of this new branch of science into numerical relation with the units of already existing practical enterprise. The electrical measuring instruments— first the electrometers, and more recently the electric current balances and other beautiful instruments for the dynamo-room and the workshop—which Lord Kelvin invented have brought the precision of the laboratory into the everyday duties of the secondary battery attendant and the wireman.

And as to methods of measurement, those who remember the haziness of even telegraph engineers as to the measurement of the efficiency of electrical currents and electromotive forces in the circuits of lamps and dynamos, in the early days of electric lighting, know how much the world is indebted to Thomson.[1] He it was who showed at first how cables were to be tested, as well as how they were to be worked ; it was his task, again, to show how instruments were to be calibrated for practical measurement of current and energy supplied by the early contractors to consumers. He had in the quiet of his laboratory long before elaborated methods of comparing resistances, and given the Wheatstone balance its secondary conductors for the comparison of low resistances ; he now showed how the same principles could be applied to measure the efficiencies of dynamos and to make up the account of charge and discharge for a secondary battery.

And if the siphon-recorder and the mariners' compass and the sounding machine proved pecuniarily profitable, the reward was that of the inventor, who has an indefeasible right to the fruit of his brain and his hand. But Lord Kelvin's activity was not confined merely to those practical things which have, to use the ordinary phrase, " money in them " ; he gave his time and energies freely to the perfecting of the harmonic analysis of the tides, undertook again, for a Committee of the British Association, the investigation of the tides

[1] The writer well remembers meeting a man of some experience in cable work who was on his way to measure the alternating currents in a Jablochkoff candle installation by the aid of an Ayrton and Perry galvanometer with steel needle !

for different parts of the world, superintended the analysis of tidal records, and invented tide-predicting machines and improved tide-gauges.

Lord Kelvin's work in the theory of heat and in the science of energy generally would have given him a title to immortality even if it had stood alone; and there can be no doubt, even in the mind of the most determined practical contemner of the Carnot cycle, of the enormous importance of these achievements. Here he was a pioneer, and yet his papers, theoretical and yet practical, written one after another in pencil and despatched, rough as they were, to be printed by the Royal Society of Edinburgh, form, as they are collected in volume i of his *Mathematical and Physical Papers*, in some respects the best treatise on thermo-dynamics at the present time! There are treatises written from a more general standpoint, which deal with complex problems of chemical and physical change of means of thermodynamic potentials, and processes which are not to be found set forth in this volume of papers; but even these are to a great extent an out-come of his "Thermoelastic, Thermomagnetic and Thermoelectric Properties of Matter."

In hydrodynamics also Lord Kelvin never lost sight of practical applications, even while pursuing the most intensely theoretical researches into the action of vortices or the propagation of waves. In his later years he worked out the theory of ship-waves with a power which has made more than one skilful and successful cultivator of this branch of science say that he was no mere mathematician, but a man who, like the prophets of old, could divine what is hid from the eyes of ordinary mortals. Of the ultimate importance of these for practical questions of the construction of ships, and the economy of fuel in their propulsion, there can be little doubt. Unhappily, the applications will have now to be made by others.

It is interesting to note that the investigation of waves in canals with which Lord Kelvin recently enriched the *Proceedings of the Royal Society of Edinburgh* have been carried out by a strikingly ingenious adaptation of the Fourier solution of the differential equation of the diffusion of heat along a bar, or of electricity along a slowly worked cable. Thus, beginning with Fourier mathematics in his earliest researches, he has in some of his last work applied the special exponential form of Fourier solution of the diffusion equation to a case, that of wave propagation, essentially different in physical nature, and distinct in mathematical signification, from that for which it was originally given.

Lord Kelvin's written work consists of the *Electrostatics and Magnetism*, three volumes of *Collected Mathematical and Physical Papers*, three of *Popular Lectures and Addresses*, the *Baltimore Lectures*, a very considerable number of papers as yet uncollected, and the *Natural Philosophy*. But this, great as it was, represented only a relatively small part of his activities. He advised public companies on special engineering and electrical questions, served on Royal Commissions, acted as consulting engineer to cable companies and other corporations, was employed as arbiter in disputes when scientific questions were involved, advocated distinctive signalling for lighthouses and devised apparatus for this purpose, and he was, above all, a great inventor. His patents are many and important. One of them was for a water-tap warranted not to drip, another, for electrical generating machines, meters, etc., was perhaps the patent of largest extent ever granted.

To Lord Kelvin's class teaching reference has been made in an earlier chapter. He was certainly inspiring to the best students. At meetings of the British Association his luminous remarks in discussion helped and encouraged younger workers, and his enthusiasm was infectious. But with the ordinary student who cannot receive or retain his mental nutriment except by a carefully studied mode of presentation, he was not so successful. He saw too much while he spoke ; new ideas or novel modes of viewing old ones presented themselves unexpectedly, associations crowded upon his mind, and he was apt to be discursive, to the perplexity of all except those whose minds were endued also with something of the same kind of physical instinct or perception. Then he was so busy with many things that he did not find time to ponder over and arrange the matter of his elementary lectures, from the point of view of the presentment most suitable to the capacity of his hearers. To the suggestion which has lately been made, that he should not have been obliged to lecture to elementary students, he would have been the first to object. As a matter of fact, in his later years he lectured to the ordinary class only twice a week, and to the higher class once. The remainder of the lectures were given by his nephew, Dr. J. T. Bottomley, who for nearly thirty years acted as his deputy as regards a great part of the routine work of the chair.

It is hardly worth while to refute the statement

often made that Lord Kelvin could not perform the operations of simple arithmetic. The truth is, that in the class-room he was too eager in the anticipation of the results of a calculation, or too busy with thoughts of what lay beyond, to be troubled with the multiplication table, and so he often appealed to his assistants for elementary information which at the moment his rapidly working mind could not be made to supply for itself.

To sum up, Lord Kelvin's scientific activity had lasted for nearly seventy years. He was born four years after Oersted made his famous discovery of the action of an electric current on a magnet, and two years before Ampère, founding on this experiment, brought forth the first great memoir on electromagnetism. Thus his life had seen the growth of modern electrical science from its real infancy to its now vigorous youth. The discoveries of Faraday in electrical induction were given to the world when Lord Kelvin was a boy, and one of the great tasks which he accomplished was to weave these discoveries together in a uniform web of mathematical theory. This theory suggested, as we have seen, new problems to be solved by experiment, which he attacked with the aid of his students in the small and meagrely equipped laboratory established sixty years ago in the Old College in the High Street. It was his lot to live to see his presentations of theory lead to new developments in his own hands and the hands of other men of genius—Helmholtz and Clerk Maxwell, for example —and to survive until these developments had led to practical applications throughout our industries, and in all the affairs of present-day life and work. His true monument will be his work and its results, and to only a few men in the world's history has such a massive and majestic memorial been reared.

He was a tireless worker. In every day of his life he was occupied with many things, but he was never cumbered. The problems of nature were ever in his mind, but he could put them aside in the press of affairs, and take them up again immediately to push them forward another stage towards solution. His "green book" was at hand on his table or in his pocket ; and whenever a moment's leisure occurred he had pencil in hand, and was deep in triple integrals and applications of Green's Theorem, that unfailing resource of physical mathematicians.

> Saepe stilum vertas quae digna legi sint
> Scripturus,

the motto which Horace recommends, was his, and he would playfully quote it, pointing to the eraser-pad in the top of his gold pencil-case. He erased, corrected, amended, and rewrote with unceasing diligence, to the dismay of his shorthand-writing secretary.

The theories and facts of electricity and magnetism, the production and propagation of waves in water or in the luminiferous ether, the structure and density of the ether itself, the relations of heat and work, the motions of the heavenly bodies, the constitution or crystals, the theory of music, the practical problems of navigation, of telegraphing under the sea, and of the electric lighting of cities—all these and more came before his mind in turn, and sometimes most of them in the course of a single day. He could turn from one thing to another, and find mental rest in diversity of mental occupation.

He would lecture from nine to ten o'clock in the morning to his ordinary class, though generally this was by no means the first scientific work of the day. At ten o'clock he passed through his laboratory and spoke to his laboratory students or to any one who might be waiting to consult him, answered some urgent letter, or gave directions to his secretary; then he walked or drove to White's workshop to immerse himself in the details of instrument construction until he was again due at the university for luncheon, or to lecture to his higher mathematical class on some such subject as the theory of the tides or the Fourier analysis.

As scientific adviser to submarine telegraph companies and other public bodies, and more recently as President of the Royal Society of London, he made frequent journeys to London. These were arranged so as to involve the minimum expenditure of time. He travelled by night when alone, and could do so with comfort, for he possessed the gift of being able to sleep well in almost any circumstances. Thus he would go to London one night, spend a busy day in all kinds of business—scientific, practical, or political— and return the next night to Glasgow, fresh and eager for work on his arrival. Here may be noticed his power of detaching himself from his environment, and of putting aside things which might well have been anxieties, and of becoming again absorbed in the problem which circumstances had made him temporarily abandon.

Genius has been said to be the power of taking infinite pains: it is that indeed, but it is also far more. Genius means ideas, intuition, a faculty of seizing by thought the hidden relations of things, and withal the power of proceeding step by step to their clear and full expression, whether in the language of mathematical analysis or in the diction of daily life. Such was the genius of Lord Kelvin; it was lofty and it was practical. He understood—for he had felt—the fascination of knowledge apart from its application to mechanical devices; he did not disdain to devote his great powers to the service of mankind. His objects of daily contemplation were the play of forces, the actions of bodies in all their varied manifestations, or, as he preferred to sum up the realm of physics, the observation and discussion of properties of matter. But his eyes were ever open to the bearing of all that he saw or discovered on the improvement of industrial appliances, to the possibility of using it to increase the comfort and safety of men, and so to augment the sum total of human happiness.

His statement, which has been so often quoted, that after fifty-five years of constant study he knew little more of electricity and magnetism than he did at the beginning of his career, is not to be taken as a confession of failure. It was, like Newton's famous declaration, an indication of his sense of the vastness of the ocean of truth and the manifoldness of the treasures which still lie within its " deep unfathomed caves." Like Newton, he had merely wandered along the shore of that great ocean, and here and there sounded its accessible depths, while its infinite expanse lay unexplored. And also like Newton—indeed like all great men—-he stood with deep reverence before the great problems of the soul and destiny of man. He believed that Nature, which he had sought all his life to know and understand, showed everywhere the handiwork of an infinite and beneficent intelligence, and he had faith that in the end all that appeared dark and perplexing would stand forth in fulness of light.

INDEX